Stirling Royal Infirmary

A History

To Christine in loving memory of her cousin "Betty Brown" Nurse, SRI.

CRAIG MAIR

Craig Mair.

NHS FORTH VALLEY

Stirling Royal Infirmary: a History
published in 2011 by

NHS Forth Valley
Carseview House
Castle Business Park
Stirling

in association with

Falkirk Local History Society

ISBN 978 0 9560480 4 2

NHS Forth Valley is extremely grateful for financial assistance
from the Society of Friends of Stirling Community Hospital
which has made production of this commemorative book
possible. If you would like to support or join the Friends, please
contact the Chairman, Allan Dewar, on 01259 750669.

Cover Design by James Hutcheson

Printed in Scotland by Bell and Bain Limited, Glasgow

Contents

Author's Note

When first invited in 2008 to write this history of Stirling Royal Infirmary I was delighted to accept, but at the time I had no idea of the challenge which would face me. Unlike the records at Falkirk and District Royal Infirmary, virtually all of Stirling Royal Infirmary's historical records have been destroyed – some apparently during a wartime paper salvage drive in 1943, but the rest more recently during service moves, when they were lost, incinerated or sent to landfill. Had Elspeth King of the Stirling Smith Art Gallery and Museum not saved a file of photographs in 2003, and Tom Whyte not rescued some documents from a medical waste skip, there might have been no surviving records at all of the hospital's colourful past.

As a result of this unexpected lack of records, I have had to gather my information from wherever it could be found. Fortunately I had a copy of Dr W G Harrington's brief history *Stirling Royal Infirmary 1874– 1974* which contains some information gained from those records now destroyed. The staff of Stirling Central Library, and at various Scottish archive collections, have also been very helpful and I extend to them my thanks. However PamMcNicol and Jane Petrie at the Stirling Council Archives have given exceptional service and, on my many visits there, have always gone the extra mile to help me track down information and illustrations. This book could not have been written without their support and professional skills.

Local newspapers have been another invaluable source of information. Older copies are held at the Stirling Council Archives and at Stirling Central Library (and have been thoroughly used), but I extend sincere thanks to Kaiya Marjoribanks of the *Stirling Observer* for her great help in digging out reports on hospital matters from the past two decades. Unfortunately photos from old newspapers have not always reproduced well, but have been used in this book when no other image was available, and I thank Jim Mailer at Whyler Photos, Stirling, for his permission to use them.

Numerous doctors, nurses and other staff, some retired but some still working, some named in the Acknowledgements and some who want to remain anonymous, have allowed me to interview them and have shared many recollections, some going back as far as the 1950s. This book would not have been possible without their memories and the better understanding which these people have given me.

Local residents and past members of the hospital staff have also provided a treasure trove of papers, photographs, old medical documents and, in one case, the original architectural drawings of the convalescent home at Chartershall, and I am extremely grateful to them. Many are listed in my acknowledgements but I would especially like to thank the Infirmary's last matron Miss Margaret Plenderleith, who allowed me to borrow many of her personal mementoes.

Hundreds of internet sites have been used, among them the American genealogical websites of past Stirling worthies such as Dr W H Forrest and the hospital's first matron Miss Helen Falconer. Through them, and especially from Tim Hall and Giles and Bob Forrest, I have obtained knowledge and photographs which I would never have found in other ways.

Although I am indebted to all who have helped me in my research, any errors, omissions or misunderstandings in the text are entirely my own.

Craig Mair
Stirling
July 2011

Acknowledgements

People interviewed: Bill Anderson, Irene Bell (nee Howatt), Dudley Booth, Betty Caddies (nee Brown), Allan Dewar, Bill Duncan, Evelyn Duncan, Chris Fawcett (nee Bell), Marguerite Gow (nee Craig), Alastair McNeill, Margaret Plenderleith, Mary Ross (nee Brown), Margaret Sherry (nee O'Connor) . . . . and many more who wish to remain anonymous.

People who have helped: Fraser Brown, Wilma Burns, Thea Denton, John Dreczkowski, Kate Fawcett, Bob Forrest, Giles Forrest, David Grinly, Tim Hall, Jim Leslie, Elma Lindsay, Robert Polson, Ian Scott, Tom Selbach, John Speake, Cara Stern, Tom Whyte, Trudy Whyle.

Also: Stirling Council Archives staff (especially Pam McNicol and Jane Petrie), Stirling Council Planning Department staff, Stirling Observer staff (especially Kaiya Marjoribanks), Stirling Central Library staff (especially Roana Mourad), Bridge of Allan Library staff, Stirling University Library staff, Smith Art Gallery and Museum staff, NHS Forth Valley staff (especially Communications Manager Kate Fawcett), Stirling Royal Infirmary staff, Forth Valley Royal Hospital staff, Highland Council Archive staff, NHS Highland Archive staff, NHS Greater Glasgow and Clyde Archive staff, Lothian Health Service Archive staff, RCAHMS staff.

A companion volume to this book, *Falkirk and District Royal Infirmary: a triumph of co-operation* by Ian Scott is being published at the same time price £9.99. It is available from NHS Forth Valley, Falkirk Local History Society (01324 627692) and bookshops.

CHAPTER ONE

The Need for a Hospital

Stirling was founded as a royal burgh by King David I in AD 1124, and along with Perth, Edinburgh and Dunfermline is one of the four oldest burghs in Scotland. The first reference to a castle at Stirling is even earlier and dates from AD 1119, so almost certainly there must have been a community of some sort at Stirling even before it officially became a burgh.

If there was a community, then there would also have been some kind of health care for the people during that time hundreds of years ago, even if it was only the old spey wife with a knowledge of herbal cures, or perhaps the barber surgeons who did a little primitive blood letting and tooth pulling in Scotland's medieval towns. Some kind of health care, perhaps, but it cannot have been much – indeed many people would have relied on little more than the mythical powers of charms or holy wells.

Unfortunately these simple health remedies were actually of little real benefit. Human life was precarious and often short in medieval times. For a start, every burgh was full of filth, even those like Stirling which were built on a slope so that the animal droppings, dungheap waste and sewage thrown out of windows eventually trickled to the bottom of the hill. In Stirling that's where the town gate aptly named the Dirt Row Port once stood. No wonder only the poor people lived there – richer people were the 'folks who lived on the hill' around Broad Street and Castlehill, well away from the muck and the smells at the bottom of King Street.

Stirling's food was also unhygienic. Meat was butchered in public with no knowledge of germs, flour was often mixed with dirt or dust, oats and barley were full of millstone grit, water was often drawn from contaminated streams, teeth were used to hold everything from bow strings to sewing needles which caused frequent abscesses, no-one washed their hands when handling food, and so on. As a result, most people were on average six inches shorter than today and were lucky to live past forty years.

On top of this were periodic outbreaks of plague. Stirling suffered several dreadful epidemics including one in 1606 which killed 600 people, perhaps half of the town's population. With each outbreak, 'plague pits' were dug beyond the walls of the old burgh, such as those where Viewforth and Bridgehaugh are now. The corpses of these sad victims were just hurriedly tossed in, with no ceremony and not even any coffins.

There was also the ever-present scourge of leprosy (from which even King Robert the Bruce may have died). Until about 1600 this was the most feared illness in Scotland, the social outcast disease of its time, for which citizens of all social rank were forced out of town if they were 'fund lipir'. Isolation 'hospitals' for lepers existed outside some burghs including Dundee, Elgin, Haddington, Aberdeen, Edinburgh and St Andrews. For a time the Augustinian monks of Cambuskenneth Abbey staffed a similar leper colony at Airthrey, at that time well outside Stirling, where they helped the unfortunate inmates with a sense of charity stronger than that of self-preservation.

Some time during the fourteenth century this hospital was replaced by a proper leper house run by the Town Council, located in the Allan Park area (also outside the burgh in those days), probably on the site of the later manse where there was spring water. Local tradition says that Robert the Bruce visited springs or wells in this Allan Park area in the hope of curing his own illness; the old belief in the healing power of wells spread right to the top of medieval society. This leper hospice was run by the Church but it was also given help from the Crown (as in 1464 when it received grain supplies).

It seems that Stirling people who were declared to be lepers were given a charitable payment of twenty shillings and sent to this leper house to be treated. If they had not recovered by the time their money ran out they were then put out to become vagrants. This probably meant having to sit begging outside the burgh gates, since they would not have been allowed back into the town for fear of infecting others. At Torphichen Priory near Linlithgow there is even a 'leper's window' which would have allowed lepers to watch religious services from outside the building – they were not even allowed into churches.

As well as staffing the first leper house at Airthrey, the monks of Cambuskenneth Abbey also had a 'hospital' in Stirling. The Hospital of St James, granted to the Augustinian monks by King Robert III in 1403, stood near the southern end of the old Stirling Bridge at

Spittalmyre, roughly where the present Orchard House medical centre stands now. The original hospital owned orchards there which survived until they were swept away by the construction of the Stirling to Balloch railway in 1856. The name 'hospital' is misleading, however. This building was more of a 'hospice' or shelter for travellers, than a hospital in the medical sense. In the days before proper inns it was common for the Church to operate such places, especially on the pilgrim routes of Europe. Sadly the building, and its neighbouring Chapel of St Roche, was destroyed during the Reformation, probably in 1559.

There were several other 'hospitals' in medieval Stirling, also run by the Church, but which also disappeared during the Reformation. Old records refer to the Queen's Hospital (perhaps founded by Mary of Gueldres but which seems to have lapsed after her death in 1463). Another was the Hospital of St Peter and St Paul, established some time before 1482 but known to have been in ruins by 1610. These may also have been for travellers, or for the poor, or even for the care of the sick, but they were not places for medical treatment.

After the Reformation the entire system of alms houses, hospices and Church-run charities disappeared. All across Scotland the lands of the Catholic Church, which had provided the revenue used to support the sick and the poor, were seized and taken into private ownership. The task of caring for the sick and needy fell instead upon the Kirk, which in Stirling was really the Kirk Session of the Holy Rude church. Each Sunday the congregation would support the needy by offering regular donations to the 'Poor Box'. This money was then used as wisely as possible by the Kirk Session to care for the sick, the elderly, the poor, the blind, the orphaned, the maimed, the unemployed and (in time of famine) the starving of the burgh.

There were two other 'hospitals' of this time in Stirling which also deserve mention, if only because they were also *not* hospitals in the medical sense. In 1530 a 'hospital' was founded by Robert Spittal, one of Stirling's greatest citizens, as a charitable hospice for respectable poor people in the town. Spittal was tailor to King James IV and especially to Queen Margaret, whose fondness for fashionable dresses kept the tailor busy and made him a rich man. Spittal's original 'hospital' was eventually opened in 1540 just outside the town walls where Irvine Place is today. It was often called the 'Nether Hospital' because it was 'nether' or lower than the town, which still clustered higher up the castle hill in those days.

ERECTED IN HONOUR OF ROBERT SPETTALL
TAYLOR TO KING IAMES THE FOURTH
DONOR OF THE HOSPITALL IN THIS BURGH
FOR RELIEF OF DECAYED TRADESMEN
THE LIBERAL MAN DEVYSET H LEBERALL
THINGS

Here in the old Grey Friers yaird stood the
Hall of the Seven Incorporated Trades of
Stirling from 1751 to 1907. TEMPORI PARENDUM

This plaque, on the Back Walk in Stirling, commemorates Robert Spittal's
hospital which stood where the Highland Hotel is now. *Photo Craig Mair*

Spittal's hospital provided about a dozen people, mostly men from
a craft or trade background or their widows, with clothes, food, heating
and cooking pots to help them survive poverty. This institution later
moved to the site of the old Grey Friars' monastery in Spittal Street,
which had been closed and its lands confiscated during the
Reformation. This same place later became the site of the High School
and is now the Highland Hotel. Nowadays a plaque to commemorate
Robert Spittal is displayed on the wall of a house in Spittal Street,
opposite the Highland Hotel, but this is misleading – the actual
hospital was across the street in the Friars' Yard which is now the
hotel. Indeed the wall plaque may even originate from the earlier
'nether' hospital building opened in 1540.

Stirling's other great benefactor was John Cowane who, at his death
in 1633, left money for the establishment of a 'hospital' in the town.
Cowane was a very successful merchant who became a burgh councillor
and bailie in 1611, Dean of Guild in 1624 and the town's member of
parliament in 1625. He also met King Charles I and Charles II several
times in connection with burgh or Scottish national affairs. On his
death he left forty thousand merks for the provision of an almshouse

or hospital for twelve 'decayed' merchants of Stirling, or their widows (known then as 'relicts'). At the time this was a very commendable but practical act of charity, for it was entirely possible for a prosperous merchant to become suddenly ruined or bankrupt. War, famine, plague, the loss of a ship, or the burning of a warehouse could easily condemn a proud middle class family to poverty. To have Cowane's hospital there 'just in case' must have been a reassurance to Stirling's strutting, proud merchants.

Work began on the construction of 'Cowane's Hospital' on a site (also gifted by Cowane) close to the Church of the Holy Rude in 1637. Although delayed by a terrible outbreak of plague in 1645, the building, complete with a statue of Cowane dressed in his merchant finery, was eventually completed and opened in 1649. It consisted of seven small bedrooms for inmates, plus a hall, a dining room, a business or charter room and accommodation for a Keeper and servants. The bedrooms were plain but were each furnished and heated by a fire complete with cooking pots and pans.

Almost immediately the building was requisitioned in 1651 by occupying English Cromwellian troops and did not really begin to

Cowane's Hospital *Photo courtesy Stirling Observer*

function as intended until the departure of the soldiers in 1660. Even then, it was not greatly used because of the required uniform and strict rules for inmates, and because (as with Spittal's hospital) most people preferred out-relief in their own homes to the social embarrassment of living in a charity institution. At no point, however, was the Hospital seen at that time as a place of medical provision.

The picture so far would seem to suggest a town in which there may have been 'hospitals', but in which there were actually no doctors or proper medical services at all. In fact, the Stirling burgh records do quite often refer to physicians, 'chirurgeons' (or surgeons) and apothecaries. In 1609, for example, the Town Council suspended Alexander Slater from 'exercising the office and cure of a chirurgeon from hence forth until they be further testified of his knowledge and sufficiency, under the pain of banishment from the burgh'. So there were doctors in Stirling.

On the other hand, this medical provision was generally only for Stirling's richer people. In 1615 when bailie John Cunningham was wounded in the course of his duties, the surgeon James Kinloch's fee was two hundred merks – a sum so large that the town council had to borrow from the common good fund, the box of court fines, the kirk's poor box, the Guildry, and sympathetic neighbours in order to pay it. Meanwhile poor people just went on suffering the typhus, malaria, rickets, syphilis, smallpox, meningitis, tuberculosis, bone fractures and other ailments which haunted their lives during the 17th and 18th centuries.

In 1599 the Faculty of Physicians and Surgeons was opened at Glasgow University, followed in 1681 by the founding of the Royal College of Physicians at Edinburgh (by which time the capital also had an Incorporated Guild of Surgeons and a Fraternity of Apothecaries). With these developments, a gradual improvement in medical knowledge and provision began to creep in to Scotland's other burghs. Stirling's burgh records refer, for example, to a Mr Francis Clerk, 'practitioner of phisick and chyrurgerie', who was allowed to erect a stall in the street on market days. It would be nice to think that, by opening this stall on market days when the crowds were in town, Clerk did so in order to offer his services to rich and poor alike – but we will never know. Nevertheless, when a 'great sickness' swept through the poor people of Stirling in September 1716, the local doctors offered their services for free, provided the town council would supply the necessary medicines. The council did this by paying half the cost from its own funds and persuading the kirk elders to pay the other half from church funds.

Evidence of improving medical skills is rare but the records do mention that in 1735 local bailie and surgeon Harry Christie was paid £18 for providing medicines and successfully treating two quarriers who were injured while building a well in the Back Row. Also, in 1743 William Christie was paid £12 for successfully setting a broken leg. So at least some doctors were competent enough to have enjoyed some success. Nevertheless, even by 1800 medicine was 'a scary combination of chance and quackery', as the BBC journalist Bruce Robinson wrote in 2010.

This improvement in medical knowledge and skills required a steady supply of corpses to the universities where medicine and anatomy were taught, and so ushered in those infamous characters the body-snatchers. In 1822 local grave-digger James McNab and another man called Daniel Mitchell were arrested and charged with body-snatching the corpse of an old woman called Mary Wotherspoon from the Holy Rude cemetery in Stirling. They were alleged to have stolen the body at the request of local medical student John Forrest, who immediately fled to Europe when news of the arrests reached him.

Before long news of this spread even to America. In South Carolina John Forrest's second cousin William Hutton Forrest, then a young man but who would one day become a great citizen of Stirling, wrote in a letter:

> I did not think that John Forrest possessed so much enterprise and courage as to raise a corpse; and I am very glad indeed to think that his thirst for Anatomy is such, as to induce him to turn resurrection man — I cannot think less of him for it. — It is that which must be done, & it is quite immaterial by whom. — More of that has been done, than was ever dreamt of, but it was more skillfully done, with fewer assistants, & at a cheaper rate. I do not think much of his knowledge of human nature, when he employs Street Rakers, grave diggers & joiners as accomplices. He will never be able to appear again in Stirling; & I think that his best plan would be to come & finish his education in an American University. There are several very eminent medical schools in the Northern states, from whence many eminent men, in their profession, have issued.

Since the absent Forrest was the main suspect, McNab and Mitchell were eventually released. However this provoked riots by hysterical locals (unnecessarily worried that the graves of their relatives might also have been robbed) which caused troops from the 77th regiment up at the castle to be called out to restore order. The soldiers ended up shooting over the heads of the rioters in Spittal Street (one bullet passed through the window of the *Stirling Journal* office) before calm returned to Stirling.

This incident, occurring at the same time as the more notorious body-snatchers Burke and Hare were selling corpses to Dr Knox at Edinburgh University, may nevertheless be indicative of the greater interest in anatomy which was growing at that time. Indeed there was another body-snatching scare in Stirling the following year, as a result of which twelve watchmen were appointed and paid for by public subscription to guard the town and its graveyards for the next two years.

As a footnote to this episode, it is worth mentioning that John Forrest, the Stirling medical student who fled to France, eventually gained his degree at Edinburgh University in 1824, became a Licentiate of the Royal College of Surgeons of Edinburgh, received a royal pardon in 1825 for his part in the body-snatching episode and went on to have a distinguished career as an army surgeon in India and South Africa.

In 1854 Forrest was sent to the Crimean War as Deputy-Inspector of Army Hospitals before being appointed Principal Medical Officer in charge of the infamous hospital at Scutari where Florence Nightingale became a legend. Here he soon resigned his post because of a kidney infection, but following his recovery he then served as a surgeon at the battles of Balaklava, Alma, Inkerman and at the siege of Sebastapol, for which 'able exertions' he was mentioned in dispatches and received several medals. Thereafter he became in 1858 the Inspector-General of Army Hospitals and in 1859 was appointed Honorary Physician to Queen Victoria. He died in 1865 leaving a very considerable estate of £18,000. Not bad for someone whose medical career began so scandalously.

It is perhaps also worth mentioning that, according to Giles Forrest, writing in a Forrest family website:

> Before the Anatomy Act of 1832, the only legal supply of corpses for anatomical purposes were those condemned to death and dissection by the courts. While in the 1700s, hundreds had been executed for trivial crimes, by the 19th century only approximately 50 people were being

hanged each year. With the expansion of the medical schools and private anatomical schools, as many as 500 cadavers were needed. This led to body-snatching to fill the shortfall. Stealing a corpse was a misdemeanor at common law, not a felony, and was therefore only punishable with fine and imprisonment, rather than transportation or execution. The trade was a sufficiently lucrative business to run the risk of detection, particularly as the authorities tended to turn a blind eye to what they considered a necessary evil.

During the 19th century public health and medical provision began more noticeably to improve. At the time numerous medical advances, such as those made in anaesthetics and antiseptic surgery, benefited the entire country, but looking back now, certain local factors were also important in pushing Stirling in particular towards improvement and change.

Dr W H Forrest as a young man, painted June 1820 in South Carolina. *Photo courtesy Bob Forrest, USA*

One of the most important of these catalysts was the return around 1825 of Dr William Hutton Forrest from South Carolina to Stirling, his birthplace. Here, aged twenty-seven, and now an Edinburgh-trained doctor and surgeon, he set up in medical practice at no 1 The Terrace (the name Pitt Terrace only began at no 6 in those days). However, this was not enough for the young man, for he spent the rest of his life also prominent in the campaign for better public health, such as cleaner streets and a sewage system. He even won election to the town council in order to crusade for a clean water supply from a proper reservoir (the Stirling Waterworks Act was eventually passed in 1848). For these 'exertions in providing a copious supply of water for the inhabitants' he was presented in May 1857 with an inscribed silver tea service, water jug and tray by a large number of fellow-citizens and friends.

More importantly, however, W H Forrest was appointed doctor in charge of the Stirling Dispensary which opened in 1831 to 'furnish gratuitously medical advice and medicines to the poor of Stirling and adjacent county'. This was funded by individual charitable subscriptions of five shillings and also by local kirk sessions, which paid for Forrest and the three physicians whom he then enlisted to help him, to attend three days a week. They dealt with all types of medical and dental complaints and distributed free medicines, purchased with the subscribed funds, to poor people.

In 1831 the first great cholera epidemic began to sweep through Britain. By the end of that year it had reached Edinburgh and eventually cholera reached Stirling in June 1832. Forrest and the other doctors, churchmen and prominent citizens who took charge of the town during this crisis had no idea of the disease's origins in contaminated drinking water, and so their efforts at prevention or even just containment failed. Beggars were driven out of town, houses were whitewashed, barrels of tar were burned to purify the air and Cowane's Hospital was converted into an emergency hospital, all to no avail.

A charity soup kitchen was opened by sympathetic richer people because the disease seemed in other towns to have affected mostly poor people. Although they did not know it, putting food into people's stomachs was a useful way of keeping cholera at bay and, indeed, no-one in Stirling caught the illness while the soup kitchen operated. Unfortunately, as a result of its success at keeping cholera away from the poor, subscriptions dwindled and the soup kitchen was closed – next day the first of 96 cases was reported to the Board of Health. Fifty-nine Stirling people eventually died of cholera in that outbreak; the first victim was Charles McFarlane of St John Street.

Forrest believed there was a link between cholera and sewage and thereafter campaigned for cleaner streets. From then on Stirling's town council became irreversibly drawn into the demand to clean up the town and improve its medical provision. The problem was that water supply, sewage pipes and street sweepers could only be paid for by an increase in local rates – which every town councillor knew was a vote-loser. In 1832 the poor had no vote and only wealthier men could vote. Richer people strongly objected to paying for civic improvements which they said would be mostly for the benefit of the poor. As a result the town council continued to be extremely reluctant to introduce any schemes which would have to be funded by local taxes. Meanwhile one hundred local people died in just one week of an influenza epidemic at Stirling in January 1837 and more followed when typhus swept the town later that same year.

The impasse between a need for local taxation and hostile rate payers was broken by the General Police Act of 1833. This national law obliged all householders of properties with a rental value of more than £10 per annum to pay local rates in order to provide a local police commissioner and a police force. As everywhere else, Stirling's unwilling Town Council and its local voters had no choice but to accept the principle of paying for a local constabulary, run by a Police Board. This law broke the mould and before long other services, notably poor relief and a Prison Board, appeared in Stirling (added to later by a School Board and a Health Board), all paid for by local taxation. This provision of the town's first police force would eventually lead to similar calls for a hospital.

In 1845 the British government passed the Poor Law Amendment (Scotland) Act, part of which dealt with providing medical care to paupers. Although it was met with much resistance by local councils, (as a result of which it was considerably modified), the Act did remove care of the poor from kirk sessions and instead created local parish, or parochial, boards across Scotland, including Stirling, to take over this task. These boards were funded by local rates (which paid for the erection and running of workhouses) but also from a government grant, awarded specifically to help pay for the medical part of caring for the poor. As a result of this, the role of the Stirling Dispensary seemed to be redundant and, at the Annual General Meeting of the Dispensary Committee held in January 1851, the Dispensary was finally closed. Importantly for the eventual founding of the Infirmary, a sum of £458 0s 2d remained in the original Dispensary's fund. This so-called 'Dispensary Money' was eventually handed over to the town council in 1866, but with the requirement that it must be 'used for an object or objects which would have in view the sanitary improvement of the town'.

For the record, in its twenty-year existence the Dispensary's doctors treated 5,266 cases. In its place Stirling's poorhouse, paid for by local rates, was eventually built in Union Street and opened in 1857, complete with accommodation for two hundred paupers. There was also a separate hospital block and a lunatic asylum block in the grounds. However, to appease irate rate-payers who objected to supporting what they often called the 'lazy' poor, the qualifications for entry to the workhouse were much stricter than the previous rules for receiving medical help from the subscription-supported Dispensary, where doctors' discretion sometimes seems to have been all that was applied.

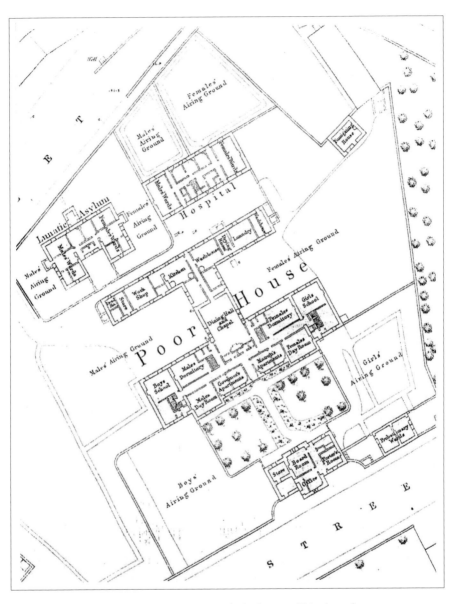

Stirling's Poorhouse in 1858, with the hospital block to the rear.
Ordnance Survey 25 inch map of Stirling, 1st edition 1858. Courtesy Stirling Council Archives

THE NEW POOR'S HOUSE: — This erection, situated at the end of the New Road, near the Bridge, is rapidly approaching completion, and it is expected will be ready for the admission of patients in November. The poor of our neighbourhood may therefore look forward to good lodgings, and such diet as the liberality of the gentlemen of the Parochial Board may extend to them. The building is fitted to accommodate about 200 paupers — a pretty fair proportion out of our population. The erection includes also an hospital, in the wards of which about 30 patients may be placed. An asylum for pauper lunatics forms also a detached feature in the building, which will accommodate about 20. Suitable houses are provided for the governor, matron, nurses and porter. A wall is to be placed around the whole structure, which in architectural design, workmanship and general fittings will, in every respect, be well adapted for the requirements of such a public charitable institution. It is in an airy and healthy situation, and in a locality which, from the contiguity of the Forth, will admit of a complete system of sanitary regulations being carried out — a matter of the first importance in any public building of this kind. The cost of the erection will be somewhere about £5000.

Report in the Stirling Observer, 4th September 1856 *Stirling Council Archives*

At a meeting of Stirling's Town Council in November 1870 the first motion that the Dispensary Money should be used to establish a local hospital was moved by councillor Thomas Muir, a successful coal merchant in Stirling. One factor which may have been in Muir's mind was that, by this time, many 'voluntary' hospitals had already been established in towns across Scotland and that Stirling was perhaps lagging behind in its provision of medical facilities.

The first voluntary hospital founded in Scotland since the Reformation was the Royal Infirmary of Edinburgh (sometimes known at that time as the Hospital for the Sick Poor), which opened in August 1729. This hospital was funded by philanthropic donations and charitable subscriptions. The original building in Robertson's

Thomas Muir around 1870. This Stirling coal merchant was first to call for the establishment of a hospital in the town.

Close had only six beds and in its first year treated thirty-five people, mostly from Edinburgh and mostly suffering from chronic conditions. A much larger and more impressive building, capable of receiving 228 patients, was opened in 1741. Originally members of the College of Physicians attended in rotation for one month per year, working free and often supplying their drugs free, but soon full-time doctors were employed – by 1766 they consisted of two physicians and four surgeons.

Thereafter, more voluntary hospitals began to appear around Scotland. At Glasgow the Town's Hospital was erected in 1733. It was also supported by public subscription including regular donations from the Town Council, the Merchants' House, the Trades' House and the Kirk Session. Eventually this was replaced by Glasgow's Royal Infirmary, which had 136 beds when it opened in December 1794 – a capacity that was improved to 208 beds when an extension was completed in 1815. The original Robert Adam building (replaced in 1914) had five floors which contained eight wards and a circular operating room on the fourth floor with a glazed dome ceiling.

Other hospitals also appeared. Aberdeen's hospital was opened in 1742 but was replaced in 1840 with a better building capable of accommodating 230 patients. Thereafter, numerous other infirmaries were opened all over Scotland, including those at Dumfries (1776), Montrose (1782), Dundee (1798), Inverness (1804), Paisley (1805), Greenock (1809), Leith (1837), Perth (1838), Ayr fever hospital (1845), Arbroath fever hospital (1845), Kirkwall (1845), Nairn (1846), Forfar (1862), Fort William (1863), St Andrews (1865), Kilmarnock (1868) and Dingwall (1872). The starting dates vary a little according to different records and data bases, but they were all there long before anything at Stirling.

Meanwhile doctors in Stirling, where there was no hospital closer than Edinburgh or Glasgow, faced very difficult conditions. For example, after the opening of railways to Stirling in the late 1840s, railway accidents began to happen surprisingly frequently, both to railway employees and to members of the public who were not used to the danger of approaching trains. When an accident occurred, local doctors Moodie and Forrest were often called and, if the patient required surgery, they were operated on in the primitive surroundings of either a railway shed or in the station's waiting room. After that the patient was either sent home to recover or, occasionally, sent by rail to the infirmaries in either Edinburgh or Glasgow.

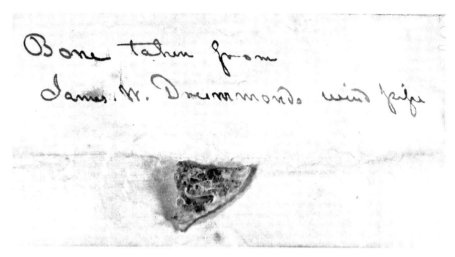

The bone which was removed from James Drummond's wind pipe by Professor
James Syme in 1853 – the first tracheotomy ever performed in Stirling.
Photo courtesy of the Stirling Smith Art Gallery and Museum

In March 1853 three-year-old James Drummond swallowed a chunk
of mutton bone which stuck in his throat. On 28th June this was
eventually removed by the famous James Syme, professor of medicine
at Edinburgh University, in what it believed to have been the first
tracheotomy ever performed at Stirling (the bone is now on display at
Stirling's Smith Art Gallery and Museum). Although a happy success
for the Drummond family (James went on to become one of Stirling's
great philanthropists in later life) the fact was that a doctor had to be
brought from Edinburgh to do this operation. This was far from ideal
or satisfactory and must surely have highlighted the lack of a hospital
in Stirling itself.

In addition, several Dispensaries were also already established long
before Stirling's was opened in 1831. They included the Royal Public
Dispensary at Edinburgh (founded in 1776). As Donald M Thomson
writes in his article *General practice and the Edinburgh Medical School: 200
years of teaching, care and research*:

> The Public Dispensary of Edinburgh, often called the Old Town Dispensary,
> flourished. Physicians and surgeons were appointed as medical officers.
> They attended weekly, accompanied by their students whose fees
> contributed, in part, to the funds of the dispensary. So it was that the
> successful medical practitioners of Edinburgh came to contribute to the

welfare of the poor in the community and to the education of medical students. Later, other branches of the dispensary opened in Edinburgh and in Leith. In 1801 it established a Vaccine Institute for the preparation and supply of lymph for smallpox vaccination.

This was surely the way forward, and more dispensaries followed, including those at Montrose (1782), Dundee (1782) and Paisley (1786).

Several 'asylums for the humane treatment of the insane' were also opened, including those at Montrose (1782), Dumfries (1791), Aberdeen (1800), the Royal Edinburgh Asylum (1809), Glasgow (1814), Dundee (1820), Perth (1827) and the Royal Scottish National Institution at Larbert, which opened in 1862. These places were a far cry from the 'common madhouse' to which unfortunate people had previously been sent, but again, there was nothing anywhere near Stirling until the opening of the poorhouse (which included an asylum block) in 1857.

Finally, there was also the innovative Royal Hospital for Sick Children at Edinburgh which opened in 1860 with space for twenty-four cots, and the Royal Maternity and Simpson Memorial hospitals for 'lying-in women' at Edinburgh, originally established (as opposed to being part of the Royal Infirmary) in 1793. By providing facilities specifically for children or expectant mothers, the lack of anything at all in Stirling must have been even more obvious.

So when councillor Thomas Muir first called for a hospital at Stirling in 1870, he did so in a Scotland which was gradually becoming better provided with medical facilities. By then a county town like Stirling really should have had a hospital too.

CHAPTER TWO

Miss Falconer's Years

1870-1900

The first reference to Stirling's eventual Royal Infirmary was in November 1870, when local coal merchant and councillor Thomas Muir proposed at a town council meeting that a hospital and dispensary should be established in Stirling. In December 1870 Muir explained this further to a meeting of the Stirling Police Commission, when he said:

> The more I think on the subject of an hospital, the more I am satisfied that it is a matter of urgent necessity – whether we take into account the state of health in our town, or whether we look at the state of health in the cities of Edinburgh or Glasgow, and the exertions put forward by the authorities or others to obtain accommodation for those in severe affliction.

Muir's intention was *not* to have a 'hospital sustained by annual subscriptions', as he put it, but rather that it would be the property of the town, provided and maintained by local ratepayers. He pointed out that the recent Public Health Act of 1867 permitted local authorities to appoint Medical Officers of Health and to raise money by rates for public health purposes. (In fact, fearing a voter backlash, few burghs had done so – neither had Stirling. Indeed, it required a second Act in 1889 to make the appointment of County medical officers of health in Scotland obligatory.)

While there seems to have been a willingness in the Town Council to support Muir's proposal, there was much concern about using local rates to pay for it. As Provost George Christie said:

> The local authority, under the Act of Parliament, has certain rating powers. I hope that the committee will not report in favour of an additional assessment in the Burgh; I shall be compelled to oppose that, because I think it is not needed, – I think it is not necessary to assess this burgh for an hospital . . . there is an abundance of funds both for charity and

education, and it is particularly appropriate in my opinion that, in apportioning these funds, to set aside a sum something like £100 per annum, in support of an hospital for the benefit of the sick poor, or other people who it is intended should get the benefit of these institutions.

Provost Christie's concern about rates was accepted, and with that concession Muir's motion was then carried, on the basis that any development would be funded by voluntary subscriptions. In February 1871 a committee was then formed to take the hospital idea further. This committee consisted of the Provost, burgh magistrates and the entire town council, with Thomas Muir as its Honorary Secretary and Treasurer. This committee's main task was to:

> .... obtain as many subscribers as possible. As soon as can be, a meeting of subscribers to be held to elect their own Chairman and Directors and otherwise to arrange their own business. On this being done, this provisional committee to fall.

In April a notice appeared in local papers outlining the plan to have a local hospital where 'the labouring man or members of his family can come at once for relief from sickness'. It appealed for more subscribers and, as an encouragement to others, printed a list of those who had already subscribed. At the top of this list came the Dispensary Money (now £496 16s 4d) and a £200 donation from the Town Council, followed by twenty-three other donors, mostly the owners of local or county estates but also including £50 from Provost Christie, £10 from Sheriff Sconce, £10 from Thomas Muir himself and five guineas from James Hogg of the *Stirling Journal and Advertiser*.

In spite of this example set by Stirling's gentry, there was in fact a very poor public response to the appeal for subscribers. When looking back at the end of that first year, the *Stirling Journal* wrote:

> Somehow or another great apathy was shown in Stirling to the proposed erection, so much so that the collectors had the utmost difficulty in dragging out the few subscriptions they got from the general public.

One of those who did show great interest was Sir David Erskine of Cardross. The story goes that, while dining as a guest at nearby Polmaise Castle, he was spoken to by a lady who 'expressed astonishment that no infirmary existed in Stirling or the surrounding district'. He seems to have agreed and thereafter began 'agitating among many friends until he got up interest in the matter'.

On 11th August 1871 (by
which time £1,768 14s 4d had
been raised) a meeting of
subscribers was held at the
Golden Lion Hotel and their first
committee and directors were
chosen. The influence of Sir
David Erskine is clearly there,
for many of those present were
from his social circle. Sir A C R
Gibson-Maitland of Sauchie
was appointed Chairman of the
Institution, with Provost
Christie as Deputy-Chairman.
The first directors were the Earl
of Dunmore, Colonel John

Provost Thomas Christie around 1870

Murray of Polmaise, Sir Henry Seton-Stewart of Touch House, John
Campbell of Inverdarroch, Major Wilson, Sir David Erskine of
Cardross, Sheriff Robert Sconce, Bailie Thomas Low, Councillor James
Hogg, local merchants Henry Drummond and James Reid and local
lawyer James Mathie. Thomas Muir was elected Secretary and Messrs
Chrystal and McFarlane were appointed Treasurers.

In December the first AGM was held in the Golden Lion Hotel, by
which time subscriptions had risen to £2,530 4s 10d towards the
erection of the building, and £182 5s 6d towards its running and
maintenance. At this meeting printed copies of the proposed
Constitution and Regulations for the Management of the Stirling
Infirmary and Dispensary were circulated and approved.

By this time several potential sites had also been considered at places
all over Stirling. These included, among others, the Gowan Hills, the
top end of Princes Street, a plot opposite the Poorhouse in Union
Street and a site at one end of Albert Place. The favoured site was at
Glencoe Road close to the Gowan Hills, but this intention came to
nothing and eventually the directors bought the old Commercial Bank
Building at the bottom end of Spittal Street, for a price of £1517 3s 3d.
This neo-Classical building, with its distinctive Doric columned
portico, originally designed by James Gillespie Graham in 1825, was
of course not yet suited to purpose and was also damp.

Map of the original hospital building and its grounds, stretching from Spittal Street to the Back Walk. *Ordnance Survey 25 inch map of Stirling, 1st edition 1858, Stirling Council Archives.*

In 1873 architects Peddie and Kinnear of Edinburgh were asked to submit a plan for the conversion of the building into a hospital for eighteen beds. John Dick Peddie and Charles Kinnear had, by this time, already accumulated an extremely impressive list of over three hundred works to their credit. Among the scores of banks, court houses, churches, hotels, schools, country mansions and other commissions already completed were Morrison's Academy in Crieff, the Aberdeen municipal buildings and tolbooth, St Enoch's railway station and hotel in Glasgow and the Caledonian railway station and hotel in Edinburgh. In 1874 they would also go on to design the Dunblane Hydropathic establishment (now, of course, the Dunblane Hydro Hotel).

By 1873 the firm was also responsible for at least some of Victorian Stirling's look, including the layout of the Valley cemetery, the Erskine Church memorial, the Royal Bank of Scotland building, the Allan Park

U.P. church, Brentham Park house at Livilands, the St Ninians manse, and the Poorhouse, which opened on Union Street in 1857. They had also come second in the design competition for the Wallace Monument.

Perhaps more importantly, Peddie and Kinnear already had experience in designing infirmaries, notably the Chalmers Hospital in Edinburgh and the Fife and Kinross District Asylum at Cupar, plus several poorhouses with medical facilities included, such as those at Inveresk, Prestonkirk and St Cuthbert's Edinburgh. As a firm which offered both the prestige of well-known architects and yet which also knew specifically about hospitals, it was a good choice.

The building of 1874 did not look as it does now. The front was only five windows wide (the two flanking wings and other additions appeared later). Entry from Spittal Street was by wide centrally placed steps which were directly in front of the Doric columns and the front door. The entire site was also tightly hemmed in by the Ragged and Industrial School and Allan's School on one side, and two plots with dilapidated tenements, pigsties and byres on the other side (with the High School playground beyond). Spittal Street was also much narrower than today, so that the grounds in front were larger than they are now, while to the rear there were gardens (including a sun dial) which stretched down to the town wall and the Back Walk.

When eventually completed, Peddie and Kinnear's conversion of the building, described as 'of a suitable nature, from its airy and healthy situation, its structure and accommodation', provided a male and female ward, each of eight beds, an additional recovery room for two females with an additional two cribs, and rooms for the resident Medical Officer, the Matron, and other staff.

On entering through the front door the male ward was a large room with a south-facing bay window on the left, while the rooms for the doctor and matron were on the right. The female ward, also with a nice bay window facing south to the sun, was directly above the male ward. The basement, which had its own entrance door below the steps of the main front door, contained a washhouse, kitchen, scullery, servants' room and a spare room for medical use – large enough perhaps to have been the 'recovery room for two females' mentioned in some records. In addition there was an out-building near Spittal Street, against the wall of the Ragged School, which was initially used as a waiting room for out-patients.

The conversion and construction work was done entirely by local tradesmen. Mason work was by Dougall and Ronald of Bannockburn, joinery work was by Messrs Kemp, Murray and Nicholson of Dumbarton Road, the slater was David McGregor of the Upper Craigs, plumbing work was by John Steel of Friars Street, plasterwork was by John Craigie of Dumbarton Road, and the painting and paper-hanging was done by Robert Bald of Murray Place. The total bill for converting the former bank building was £613 2s 10d.

As alterations to the old bank building commenced, the directors also began to draw up their first by-laws and regulations for the management of the hospital. Perhaps the most important decision was that they '. . . resolved that the House Surgeon should be a young qualified medical gentleman whose services shall be entirely confined to the work of the Dispensary and Infirmary and he should be debarred from private practice.'

He was to be assisted by those local physicians and surgeons who had agreed to offer their services – they would organise a rota amongst themselves so that one would attend the infirmary every day, first to go through the wards with the house surgeon and then to the dispensary where they would '...advise with the House Surgeon in the treatment of any particular out-patients'. At that time there were ten doctors living and practising in Stirling and eight 'nurses' of whom two were midwives, but they normally worked privately, attending wealthier people in their own homes. It could not be taken for granted that any of them would voluntarily offer their services, unpaid, to the hospital, so it was vital to have at least one full-time doctor working exclusively at the hospital.

Another important resolution made by the directors was a decision not to treat fevers at the infirmary. Public feeling, whether ill-informed or not, was that contagious diseases would spread from the hospital into the town. At this time scarlet fever was sweeping through Stirling (Thomas Muir, for example, lost two of his grandchildren in 1872) and so, to avoid public outcry, the directors agreed to delete the words 'fever and other diseases' from their constitution. It was some years before any fever provision was opened, and when it was, it was at Bannockburn.

By April 1874 the first staff had been appointed. The first Matron was 33 year old Miss Helen Falconer, a native of Croy, near Inverness. Her father, who had been the school master at Croy for 50 years, had just died (indeed she carved a beautiful wooden font for the church at Croy in his memory), so, with her mother already deceased some years earlier, she was perhaps free to make her own career in life.

She came to the hospital from the Royal Infirmary at Edinburgh, where she was Head Nurse (or Ward Nurse) for Ward 16, a male ward. More importantly, she brought with her such excellent testimonials that there was 'nobody who would not have been proud of them' as Sir Alan Seton Steuart of Touch said later. Although she was described to the subscribers' AGM of 1874 as a 'matron of great experience', her starting salary was a rather meagre £26 per year, which was less than a female mill worker would have earned (and was not much more than the £23 and 8 shillings per year

Font at Croy Kirk near Inverness carved in memory of her father by Helen Falconer, just before being appointed as Stirling's first Matron in 1874. The church is now closed and the whereabouts of the font are unknown. *Photo courtesy Tim Hall, USA*

which she had earned at Edinburgh) but it was all that the board could afford from their funds.

The first Medical Officer was local physician Dr Alexander Moodie who agreed to take charge meantime until a proper house surgeon could be found – in fact he did so for about ten weeks, until the appointment of Dr Graham Steel. On moving in, Dr Steel, an 1872 graduate of Edinburgh University who had first worked as resident physician at Edinburgh Infirmary, 'reported that the most desirable mode of procuring drugs, etc., was to have a laboratory and keep a supply of drugs on the premises, and he was authorised to procure the necessary medicines and apparatus'.

Unfortunately Dr Steel resigned before the end of 1874 and was replaced by Dr John H Scott. He then moved on to Edinburgh Infirmary during 1875 and was, in turn, replaced by Dr Archibald Renny who stayed in post for the next three years. Interestingly, the first two Medical Officers, Doctors Steel and Scott, received two of the four gold medals awarded by Edinburgh University in 1877; Dr Scott then went on to become professor of anatomy at Otago University in 1877, which says much for the calibre of young doctors who were first recruited to Stirling Royal Infirmary.

Dr William H Forrest, believed to date from the 1870s. One of Stirling's great citizens. *Photo Bob Forrest, USA*

The Medical Officer and Matron were assisted by local doctors who took turns to attend the hospital, normally at 11am when they would accompany the Medical Officer round the wards and then attend the Dispensary. Dr Moodie, who had helped out during the first few weeks, continued to attend operations and consultations, but Dr William Johnston and the redoubtable William Forrest (until his death in 1879) also regularly took turns and were later also joined by a Dr Stewart (probably D P Stewart, who had previously been an assistant surgeon with the Stirlingshire Militia).

Later in life Miss Falconer described these early days:

> The wards were comfortably furnished and everything was got that was necessary for the patients and the work. But alas for the house surgeon's and matron's apartments! The former had not one room he could feel was his own. The room which was supposed to be his sitting room did duty as Boardroom, and the out-patients were seen in it, and the drugs were kept and dispensed from his bedroom. There was only one room could be given to the matron and her nursing staff, which meant that I could not have any one to help in night or day nursing unless the nurse occupied this one room with me. I got my sister [Isabella], still in her teens, for my first help. Unfortunately she became matron at Inverness Infirmary. I then got Nurse Edgar ... She was twenty years in the Infirmary, and a great help to me. Dr Moodie was surgeon in the first year of the Infirmary's existence, helped by Dr Forrest.

These doctors gave their time and skills gratis, but even the staff who were fully employed at the hospital did not earn much. Even by 1877 the entire bill for hospital salaries and wages for a year was only £210 9s 9d.

According to the directors' minutes of that time, on the day before opening Matron was instructed to make an inventory of all furniture, table linen and bed linen. Some necessities were evidently not yet in place, and at the last minute such things as a clock, door mats, weights and scales, a laundry mangle and wringer, a servant's bed and bedding, a waterproof cloth for the operating table, and Venetian blinds for windows facing the street were all hurriedly bought. Even then, a week later there was another urgent purchase of cups and saucers, teapots, 'drinking jars', food trays, milk bowls, extra sheets and 'one tureen for Surgeon'.

Meanwhile the Clerk had five hundred letters of recommendation for in-patients printed. Each subscriber of £1 or more then received three of these letters, which allowed them to nominate someone requiring hospital in-patient care (although it is interesting to note that one of the first in-patients was a local landowner who was brought with a bleeding nose). Each donor of five shillings (25p) or more received six letters of recommendation for people to receive out-patient treatment. These letters were supposed to be used only for recommending someone from the 'deserving poor' for treatment but for many years there were protests from the directors that this was abused.

The infirmary (or 'Institution' as it was often called at that time) was supposed to have opened on Monday 15th June but this was delayed because the interior walls were still damp. It finally opened 'for the reception of patients' on Tuesday 16th June 1874. There was no opening ceremony (unlike the Smith Art Gallery and Museum a few weeks later, when even the shops closed to allow people to attend the opening ceremony). In the case of the infirmary, as with the completion of the new Stirling Bridge in 1833, there was no fuss and people simply started using it.

In its first six months the hospital treated sixty in-patients and 325 out-patients. Of the in-patients (drawn from all over the district), seventeen were treated for accidents (although some of these were serious cases) and the remaining forty-three were medical and surgical cases. The first surgical case was in later July 1874 when a man's hand, 'irreparably injured' by an accident, was successfully amputated.

The first out-patient was a lad called George Henderson from Lower Bridge Street. Writing much later from his home in Australia, he recalled: 'We Gowan Hill boys were always at war with the Castlehill boys. In one of the engagements I got my head opened by a half brick thrown by one of the Castlehills. After a while I wakened and saw what I thought was an angel, but I afterwards learned I was in the Infirmary and the angel was Miss Falconer. She was an angel to me, and I will never forget her kindness'.

Almost all the out-patients were local poorer people. They often included children, among them a girl who had two fingers amputated after an accident, and a 'waif' who was knocked over by fighting dogs and suffered a broken leg. Numerous injuries were also caused by either farm machinery or railways and the various railway companies, such as the North British and the Caledonian, which both operated through Stirling, became early subscribers to the hospital.

From the outset the hospital sourced its needs from local suppliers. Invoices for 1874 show that bread was supplied by Torrance the bakers, milk came from Mrs Watt's dairy in Spittal Street, crockery from Alexander Baird and son, general groceries from D and J MacEwan's shop in Port Street and butcher meat from W and J Cullens. By late August, however, the more established Baker Street firm of James Finlayson had won the meat concession by offering to supply roast beef and steak at ten pence per pound and boiling beef at ninepence per pound. Finlayson also supplied beef tea (similar to Bovril) which was made, evidently in his shop, by steeping cubes of grilled beef in jars filled with water, which were then gently heated in water to produce the nourishing beef essence. This was considered a very suitable drink for convalescing patients.

As life and work at the hospital began to settle down, adjustments began to be made. The patients needed amusements, and a solitaire board donated by bailie R S Shearer was gratefully acknowledged. Local ladies also began a rota of visits, and flowers, fruit, books and toys began to appear in wards, 'to break the monotony of the sick room' as the papers put it. More staff were soon required and the Secretary was instructed to advertise in the local papers for an assistant nurse. Although ' . . . none under 30 need apply', experience was not considered necessary but good character was deemed 'indispensable'. In addition a washerwoman was employed two days a week to do the hospital's laundry. An interesting quantity of alcohol also began to be required; the minutes refer to a supply of beer and a dozen bottles of sherry for the surgeon's use, and a gallon of whisky 'to be used as a stimulant for patients'.

These developments must have increased the hospital's running costs, for within six weeks of opening the Secretary was also drafting a letter to local clergymen seeking church door collections towards the hospital's funds. As the *Stirling Journal* reported, the initial appeal for subscribers had been 'coldly received by the inhabitants of this town' and it joined in urging local and county churches now to reverse that attitude and to help support the hospital's running costs. In mid-September the first church donation (of £11) was made by the Church of Scotland at St Ninians, followed in October by the Roman Catholic chapel in Irvine Place which donated £6 10s. Gradually many more local churches, of all Christian denominations, followed suit and eventually an annual Hospital Sunday even began, on which day there was a special drive to raise funds in churches across the area. By 1878 thirty-seven congregations were contributing in this way.

Then in late November 1874 the Directors received a letter from the Home Secretary which read:

Whitehall
23rd November, 1874

My Lord,
I have the honour to inform Your Lordship, in reference to Your Lordship's letter of the 11th instant, that Her Majesty has been graciously pleased to signify Her Approval that the Infirmary of Stirling shall in future be styled the "Royal Infirmary of Stirling."

I have the honour to be
My Lord,
Your Lordship's obedient servant
The Marquis of Hertford
Ragley Hall, Alcester.

The *Stirling Journal*, always keen to promote the hospital to an unenthusiastic population, seized on this event and wrote:

> This mark of royal favour will no doubt be fully appreciated by the inhabitants of Stirling, not only as proof of Her Majesty's anxiety for the welfare of her subjects, but also as a token of her interest in a town so closely associated with her royal ancestors.

And so the hospital received the name which it was to carry from then on, for the next 137 years. Soon the letters ROYAL INFIRMARY were displayed proudly above the entrance columns. Indeed, even when the hospital moved to new premises in 1928 and the letters were taken down, the fixture holes remained

The original letter granting royal status to Stirling's Infirmary now hangs in the Board Room of NHS Forth Valley.

there, still silently spelling out the name until the building's conversion to a hotel in 2011.

During 1875 the infirmary handled 117 in-patients and 3555 out-patients, of which total only four died (and they were 'all considered hopeless when admitted'). By 1876 the figures had risen to 158 in-patients, on whom 'many difficult and important operations were successfully performed' and of whom nine died (six of which were 'expected'). By 1877 the number of in-patients was up again to 166, of whom 104 were surgical cases.

Lurking behind these pleasing figures was the constant battle to raise enough money to keep the infirmary going. In 1876 a fundraising concert was held at the Smith Art Gallery and Museum, which raised £90. This concert was repeated in Dunblane and raised another £24. In 1877 income from individual subscriptions was £455 18s 9d, while the money raised by local churches was around £145 (a very respectable part of the approximately £800 needed that year to maintain and run the hospital). In addition, numerous local craft firms, trades, shops, banks, railway companies and others with employees who might benefit from hospital treatment when required, took out 'public body' subscriptions, as did various Lodges, football clubs, the Stirling Guildry, the Incorporation of Shoemakers, the Cowane Hospital and others for their members. Nevertheless, the struggle to match income to expenditure featured in the report at every shareholders' AGM for many years. As one speaker put it, "We crave not the large subscriptions from the few but the small subscriptions from the many".

As the 19th century progressed the Royal Infirmary progressed with it. For example, by 1877 religious services for in-patients were being held there by a variety of local churchmen, who agreed that while they might debate their different interpretations of the Christian faith, they were united in their desire to serve the patients at the hospital.

A few of the more quirky insights to life at the Infirmary have also survived from the 1870s. For example, it seems that visitors had to remove their shoes on entry to the building. It seems also that the Infirmary kept its own cows at Dalgleish Court (just off Baker Street) in order to ensure a fresh supply of milk. The nursing staff at this time consisted of the Matron (Miss Falconer), an Assistant Matron (Miss Edgar) and two maids – who were also expected to act as night nurses!

In 1878 improvements were made to ventilation in the hospital, on account of a concern that the skin infection erysipelas would spread through the wards. As a result, the external building used as a waiting and consulting room for out-patients was converted into an isolation ward for contagious diseases. A new waiting and consulting room was then built and the hospital's entrance hall was adapted to have a dispensary where medicines could be given to out-patients. During this year Dr Renny left for a government colonial post in Ceylon and was replaced by Dr John B Robertson who served nine years at the infirmary before leaving to go into general practice in Stirling.

In 1880 (still only six years since the hospital had opened) a new appeal for funds was launched in order to provide better facilities. Up to then, for example, surgical operations had usually been performed in the wards themselves, or in the separate waiting and consulting room (or, according to one source, sometimes in a basement room). The appeal raised £1,600 and in 1882 local architect William Simpson (who had just designed both the Albert Halls and the Museum Hall at Bridge of Allan in 1881) was engaged to design the improvements 'without injuring the architectural proportions of the present building'. With room only to the east of the hospital, a new wing was built to the wall of the neighbouring Ragged School – the first step in the evolution of the building's frontage to its present appearance. The wing seems to have contained an 'isolated ward', an operating theatre and a nurses' room. Meanwhile another enlargement containing 'two large airy wards' was built as an extension wing into the ground at the back of the hospital. This ended halfway down the garden at two striking circular stair towers (which still survive). A wash-house and mortuary were also added to the bottom of the garden. These new facilities were duly opened in August 1883.

When the new wards opened it seems that they did not have enough furnishings, so Miss Falconer set about remedying this lack by raising funds to equip the wards herself. In just one month she collected an amazing £470 (eighteen times her own annual salary) to furnish the wards to her satisfaction.

In 1884 a 'speaking tube and an electric bell to communicate with the isolated ward' was fitted. This must have been a useful addition, but in 1886 a 'telephonic connection' was then donated by the National Telephone Company Ltd, free of all charge, which allowed 'connection with Bridge of Allan, Alloa and other parts of the town, and would be of advantage in giving the Infirmary authorisation to prepare for accidents in the time of emergency'. The National Telephone Company was, at this time (just ten years after the telephone's invention by Alexander Graham Bell), trying to expand into central Scotland and may have provided this phone for publicity, but it continued the service for many years, to the great benefit of the hospital.

By the 1880s the medical work of the hospital was becoming considerable. By the tenth anniversary of the opening of the infirmary nearly 19,000 patients had been treated, of whom nearly 2,000 were in-patients, mostly requiring surgery. Some procedures had been very prolonged and complex but most had resulted in successful recovery. One example was the ten year old boy who, playing on the railway line at Causewayhead, had been hit by a train and had required the amputation of both legs and an arm but was now convalescing.

In addition, very few years recorded more than ten deaths at the hospital and the figure was often only three or four. Of the deaths which did occur, many were regarded as 'hopeless accident cases on arrival never considered likely to survive'. One instance was the dreadful explosion of a boiler at Davie and Sons' foundry at Orchard Place in April 1883; three men were killed instantly but were nevertheless taken to the Infirmary where they became three of the nine deaths recorded at the hospital that year. On the other hand, two others, who were so badly injured in the same explosion as to be considered hopeless, did recover at the hospital.

There is no doubt that the work of the hospital was very appreciated in the town. In 1885, for example, employees of the Caledonian Railway Company made a special presentation to Miss Falconer. Headed by Mr James Samuel the stationmaster, they gathered in the Board Room to hand over a handsome marble clock and an engraved silver pencil case, 'in recognition of your unremitting and devoted zeal and attention, and your sympathetic kindness to those servants of the company who, through accidents or from other causes have, from time to time, during the past eleven years, been patients in the Infirmary', as Mr Samuel said.

Miss Falconer seems also to have had an interest in conditions for working men beyond the hospital. In 1887 the *Library Chronicle* reported:

> Stirling. – A public meeting of masters and workmen was held in the lesser Public Hall on June 2 to consider a scheme prepared by Miss Falconer, matron of the Royal Infirmary, and others, for the erection of a building to contain a Reading room, bath room, and other rooms for use of the working classes in Stirling. After a long discussion a Committee was appointed to consider and report to a future meeting the result.

It must be remembered that the infirmary was a subscription hospital, dependant on public donations and with its resources carefully husbanded and run by a management committee (now headed by Sir David Erskine of Cardross, who replaced Sir A C R Gibson Maitland in 1876 and, remarkably, continued in that post until 1921). Finances had to be very carefully controlled. This is excellently shown in W G Harrington's book *Stirling Royal Infirmary 1874 – 1974* where he quotes the notes of a meeting held in December 1884:

> Special meeting on expenditure. Miss Falconer reports that expenditure including food, house-keeping, gardening, to be 10¼d. per head per day for all patients and staff at the Infirmary.

In future, separate accounts for:

1.   House
2.   House-keeping, cleaning materials, etc
3.   Stimulants and Soda Water, Coal and Gas
4.   Garden

In spite of tight controls over expenditure, the directors could clearly foresee a time when the hospital would need to expand, so they began to acquire more land around the building. In 1886 and 1890 they bought the two narrow strips of land which lay between them and the High School. As a result, they now owned the entire plot of land between the High School and Allan's School, stretching from Spittal Street at the front to the Back Walk and old town wall to the rear. These boundaries are the same as those now redeveloped and occupied by the Colessio Hotel in 2011.

These newly-acquired lands included tenements on Spittal Street with dilapidated pigsties and byres behind, so in a carefully costed programme over several years these were gradually demolished and cleared. With several influential ex-provosts and councillors on the board of directors, it was then possible to have Spittal Street widened at that point.

Modifications were also made to the front garden area. In particular, local seedsman Henry Drummond donated many shrubs, but the records also mention 'Trees to be chopped down at the front of the Institution and shrubs planted, summer house to be cemented and a garden seat with chains to be provided. Plum trees to be planted against the upper wall.'

By this time more landowners of local estates were becoming involved in supporting the hospital, and names like Stirling of Garden, Graham of Coldoch, Stirling of Kippendavie, Hay Drummond of Cromlix, Campbell of Ochtertyre and others began to be listed with more established names among those attending the AGM each winter. Bequests and legacies also began to occur, including £400 from a Mrs Bain of Blairlogie in 1887 (for which one of the wards was named 'Bain's Ward') and a remarkable bequest of £2,689 in 1894 from Miss Janet Crawford Dunn of Fintry. Several entertainments also helped to augment the hospital's income, such as the Stirling Amateur Operatic Society's concert in 1890 at the Albert Hall or the £42 collected in 1888 'for admission to Airthrey Loch during eight days last winter when it was in condition for skating', as the AGM reported.

In late 1887 house surgeon John Robertson resigned to become a local GP and was replaced by Dr McNicol. He served five years, during which time further noteworthy changes occurred.

In 1891 the Annual Report noted (with just a hint of concern) that a Jubilee Nurse had begun work in Stirling. Established on the occasion of Queen Victoria's golden jubilee in 1887, this national voluntary organisation provided community nurses for poorer people in their own homes. Jubilee Nurses became highly respected figures, well known for their uniform, capes, and the bicycles on which they carried their nursing bags to patients' homes.

According to the AGM report of November 1891:

> The Directors wish it to be understood that they hail with satisfaction any efforts in the same direction . . . for the benefit and relief of the sick. They believe that there is ample work for both, and though they would have been glad if the two institutions could have been affiliated, they wish the Jubilee Nurse every success, and will be glad if she is able to take any cases which cannot remain longer in the Infirmary and are capable of treatment at home.

Nevertheless, it is interesting to note that soon after, in April 1892, the Infirmary began its own programme for training nurses, soon hailed in the local newspapers as having 'the greatest possible success'. One young lady was taken on each year, paying £12 to be trained for three months and then working as a probationer. In 1894 the first of these young ladies completed her probationary time and duly went out into the world to find a career as a 'regularly trained and certificated nurse'. Thereafter a steady flow of trainee nurses began, or as the directors put it, 'nursing in the Infirmary is now on a permanent and satisfactory basis'.

By now the hospital had grown to about twenty-two beds (of which twenty were generally occupied), and the staff had increased to the House Surgeon (Dr Murray), Matron (Miss Falconer), a Staff Nurse (Miss Edgar), a night nurse, two probationers and a ward maid. According to the Directors' report of November 1893, Dr Murray, who had replaced Dr McNicol in early 1893, 'simply devotes his whole life to the work and is hardly ever out of the Infirmary'. He was, however, still supported by the indefatigable Dr William Johnston, now in his twentieth year of voluntary help to the hospital, and who was eventually given an advisory seat on the Board.

Dr Johnston seems to have been an immense help to the Infirmary. In her retiral speech in 1901 Miss Falconer made special mention of this man:

> No matter what castle or villa required his services, the Infirmary came first, true to the teaching of his Edinburgh masters [ie university teachers]. He visited the Infirmary daily at 10.15, going from bed to bed, seeing the dressings done, advising the house surgeon and cheering the patients in his own way. When a serious accident came he was sent for immediately and, night and day, in all weathers, he came. He was with us as soon as the messenger. He did not operate himself, but he decided what was to be done and his long experience was of immense value in that way.

In 1896 a new operating theatre was completed, prompted by a concern that the previous one had insufficient lighting to let surgeons really see what they were doing. This new facility, projecting into the garden at the rear of the hospital, was mainly paid for by a 'charity entertainment' which raised £101 18s 4d in 1895, and by the fact that the floor tiles were donated and laid free. The room had a large glass roof above the operating table which certainly did improve the surgeon's view of his work. The directors portrayed this as the latest, best equipped, operating theatre but, of course, there were still no masks, gloves or hair coverings. Indeed, it was not until 1898 that an 'Anaesthetist to the Institution' was even appointed, and even then the position was unpaid and was taken in turns by local doctors.

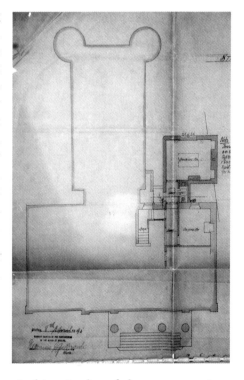

Architect's plan of the new operating theatre, built to the rear of the hospital in 1895-6. Note that the hospital building has only been extended sideways to the left, and to the rear. The operating room had a glass roof. *Photo: Stirling Council Archives*

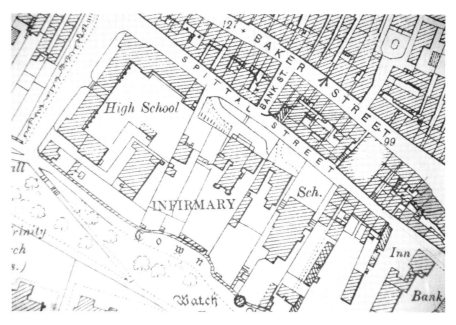

The Infirmary after the addition of the new operating theatre in 1895. William Simpson's additions of 1882 are also seen, both the wing projecting to the Ragged School and the wing projecting into the garden. From OS map MP/OS/IR/4 (1911). *Stirling Council Archives*

Nevertheless, by 1900 the hospital had undoubtedly come a long way. It was already, after only twenty-six years, a very different place from the one which had opened in June 1874. Apart from the perennial quest for subscriptions and donations, the directors and staff had every reason to look forward to the dawn of a new century with confidence and optimism.

This photograph, from William Drysdale's book 'Old Faces, Old Places and Old Stories of Stirling' (1898) commemorates local doctors, A Johnston, R Harvey, A Beath, W M Forrest and D Findlay, who served the Infirmary in its early days.

CHAPTER THREE

Miss Peebles' Years

1900-1926

With the opening of a new century, a flurry of events began to occur in Stirling's healthcare provision. In particular there was an upsurge of concern about fevers in the town. Scarlet fever, enteric fever, diphtheria, smallpox, tuberculosis and other infectious illnesses were still relatively common. Since there were no fever wards at Stirling Royal Infirmary, Stirling County Council had already opened a small 16-bed 'Fever Hospital' at Bannockburn (which later became the Bannockburn Hospital) on 17th November 1894 under Matron Miss Agnes Dempster. This was built on land sold at just £1 per acre by county councillor Sir James Maitland, and the entire cost of the project was £3000. Although this now offered some small provision for enteric and scarlet fevers and diphtheria (73 cases were admitted during its first year), public concern nevertheless increased in 1900 when a smallpox epidemic swept through Glasgow and some cases began to spread to Stirling.

By February 1901 local doctors were being urged to vaccinate free of charge any poorer residents who had not yet been vaccinated. The Town Council agreed to reimburse the cost of two shillings per vaccination to any doctors who did so. The uptake seems to have been good but nevertheless four cases of smallpox soon occurred and by the end of the year forty-five people in the town had died of TB.

By now a Stirling Combination Hospital Board had recently been established, which brought together the resources of the Stirling, Bridge of Allan, Dunblane, Callander and Doune town councils. It was already looking to provide an isolation hospital in the area, in the same way that the Stirling Combination Poorhouse (or 'Union') served the Parochial Boards of many surrounding towns, ranging from Kilsyth and Denny to Dollar and Dunblane, at its building on Union Street. During the late 1890s the Stirling Combination Hospital Board had

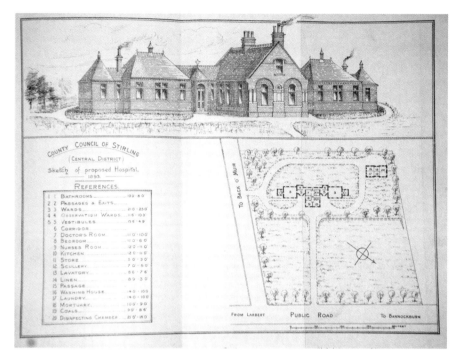

Sketch of the proposed Bannockburn Fever Hospital, 1893
Picture courtesy of Stirling Council Archives

Bannockburn Fever Hospital's original horse-drawn ambulance, used from 1894 to 1920. Pictured with the wagon and driver are the first matron Miss Agnes Dempster and her staff. *Picture courtesy of the Stirling Observer.*

already begun negotiating with the Local Government Board in Edinburgh for permission to purchase land for the construction of an Infectious Diseases Hospital on the Drip Road at Kildean (then still considered a safe distance across open fields from the nearest outskirts of Stirling at Back o' Hill). By 1900 four acres of land for the proposed hospital had been acquired but there was not yet any building.

Meanwhile, in urgent response to the threat of smallpox in 1900, Stirling Town Council hastily erected, around November 1900, a temporary isolation hospital on the Combination Hospital Board's newly-acquired land

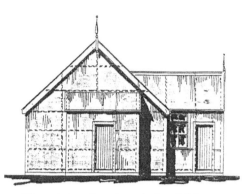

The original 'iron hospital' at Kildean.
Stirling Council Archives

at Kildean. Made of corrugated iron with a felt lining, and variously called either the 'Fever Hospital' or the 'Smallpox Hospital' by the press, it was immediately nicknamed the 'Iron Hospital' by everyone else and the name eventually stuck. It contained two four-bed wards, each with a central stove and a separate toilet, plus a kitchen and a nurse's room, and seems to have been completed in late 1900. By February 1901 the first smallpox cases were being treated there.

Meanwhile the Combination Hospital Board continued with its intention to erect a proper isolation hospital on their Kildean site. By

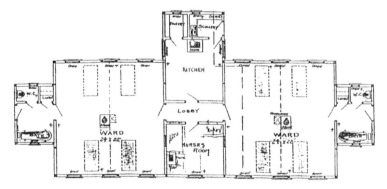

Layout of the original 'iron hospital'. Later this building became the observation and diphtheria block at Kildean. *Picture courtesy of Stirling Council Archives.*

1902 plans were produced by local architect Ebeneezer Simpson, son of William Simpson who had designed Stirling Royal Infirmary's extension in 1882, and who himself had recently designed part of the Wolfs Craig building on Dumbarton Road in Stirling.

The isolation hospital buildings, which cost £15,000 to construct, were partly modelled on those at the Lennox hospital. They consisted of a gatehouse, an administrative block (with a large kitchen, dining and sitting rooms, a dispensary, servants' rooms, and rooms for five nurses and a matron), a laundry block (which included wash houses, the heating furnace, mortuary, stables and disinfecting facilities) and separate pavilions for the treatment of Scarlet Fever and Enteric Fever. These buildings are still there, although now used for different purposes – when viewed from the street, the Scarlet Fever block is on the right and is faced by the Enteric Fever block on the left. The temporary 'Iron Hospital' was also retained as a Diphtheria and Observation block. The Scarlet Fever block had thirteen beds and the Enteric Fever block had nine beds which, with those in the 'Iron Hospital', provided approximately one bed per thousand of the local area's population. This followed the advice of Dr John C McVail, Medical Officer of Health for the counties of Stirling and Dumbarton, who was main consultant for the project.

Kildean Hospital today, not so different from its appearance in 1904. This view shows the former admin. block with the old scarlet fever block beyond. *Photo by David Grinly*

Ground floor plan of the original administration block at Kildean, 1904.
Picture courtesy of Stirling Council Archives

The hospital was opened on Thursday 9th June 1904 at a ceremony attended by town councillors and ladies of the 'combining burghs', plus various local officials and medical people. These guests were all brought to Kildean in a special procession of carriages which began at the Post Office in Stirling. During the ceremony, which was held in the Scarlet Fever Ward, the provost of Doune, the Rev G S Mackay, made a dedicatory prayer and Mr B Reynolds, builder and main contractor of the work, presented Bailie Ferguson with a gold key 'as a souvenir of the occasion and mark of their esteem' (as the Stirling Combination Hospital minutes later put it). Bailie Ferguson then made a short speech and declared the hospital open. Tea was served and the party then made an inspection tour of the hospital.

The need for the Kildean Hospital was soon apparent. According to Matron Miss Clark's annual report for 1906, the hospital treated ninety-five cases between May 1905 and May 1906, totalling 3140 days in hospital. Half of these were for scarlet fever and most of the others were for diphtheria, but there were also a few other cases of typhoid, erysipelas and measles. There were four deaths during that period, all from diphtheria, but considering that there were no fever facilities at Stirling Royal Infirmary, the decision of the Town Council to establish the Kildean Hospital was vindicated.

Meanwhile there was still no provision for smallpox cases in Stirling, in spite of the fact that there had been an outbreak in 1900-01 and that an isolation hospital had been built at Kildean. In certain circumstances Knightswood Hospital in Glasgow was prepared to accept cases from Stirling, and there was also the emergency possibility of using the Iron Hospital, but as a long-term solution there were strong objections to this from the Local Government Board in Edinburgh. By January 1904 Stirling's town council was therefore looking round for another suitable site for a specific smallpox isolation hospital.

By April 1904 the Town Council had identified Upper Taylorton Farm, situated beside the River Forth on the east side of Stirling, where they acquired an acre of ground from the Stirling Education Trust on a 30 year lease at £8 per annum. By February 1905 plans for a brick-built hospital, designed by Stirling's burgh surveyor Andrew H Goudie, had been approved by the combination burghs and by the Local Government Board. The Taylorton Hospital finally opened in early 1906. It consisted of a pavilion of two 4-bed wards for males and females, a separate building with a kitchen/sitting room and three bedrooms for staff, and another block which housed the laundry, washing house, disinfecting room and other stores. Although it cost £1200 it was 'hoped the hospital will be seldom used' as the local Medical Officer of Health put it.

Taylorton Hospital, now Lower Taylorton farm, is it looks today. This view shows the hospital building of two four-bed wards. The date above the door is 1905.
Photo Craig Mair, with permission from the occupants.

The nurses' accommodation building at Taylorton Hospital as it looks today.
Photo Craig Mair, with permission from the occupants.

While these developments were going on elsewhere in Stirling through the initiative of the Town Council, they were only for the treatment of fever cases. The Royal Infirmary continued to provide the only general medical hospital care in the area. For example, while the Combination Hospital at Kildean was treating ninety-five patients during 1905-06, the Infirmary accepted 355 in-patients and dealt with 2191 out-patients.

In October 1901 Miss Helen Falconer retired after twenty-eight years of dedicated and excellent service as Matron. On hearing the news of her decision, the local papers were full of praise for her work. The *Stirling Journal* wrote:

When she first assumed office the directors under whom she worked were almost entirely ignorant of Infirmary administration, and it was naturally left to her to organise the internal arrangements of the new infirmary and establish it on a proper working basis. This difficult duty she fulfilled with conspicuous success. The domestic department was administered with marvellous economy combined with the highest efficiency, while under her capable and experienced oversight the work of the nursing staff in the wards was equally thorough and successful. When a hospital is opened in a new district one of the chief barriers to success lies in the strong prejudice against it of the very classes it is intended to benefit. From the very first Miss Falconer set herself to break down this prejudice and show its groundlessness with the result that today there is not a working-class family in the town or surrounding district that is not but too glad to entrust their nearest and dearest to Stirling Royal Infirmary.

A campaign led by Sir David Erskine of Cardross enabled Miss Falconer to retire with a pension of £35 a year (called a 'retiring allowance' at that time, since proper state-funded old age pensions did not begin until 1908). This was followed by a public meeting held at the YMCA Institute where Provost Thomson certainly spoke for many when he said, 'From its foundation your life has been devoted to the interests of the infirmary, and with your aid you have had the satisfaction of seeing it steadily gaining the confidence of the public and the gratitude of an ever-increasing number of patients.' She was also presented by with an illuminated address and a cheque, raised by public subscription, for £375, which a grateful Miss Falconer said would 'help to keep the wolf from the door'. She died at Inverness in 1918 aged 77 and one day.

Helen Falconer was replaced by Miss Jane Peebles who won the job of Matron ahead of sixty-eight other applicants, and who quickly began to introduce some of her own ideas to the running of the hospital.

One change which soon appeared was a rearrangement of visiting hours, evidently to give more peace to those who needed tranquillity for recovery. They now became: Sunday 3-4pm, Monday, Wednesday and Friday 2-3pm, Tuesday and Thursday 6-7pm, Saturday 4-5pm.

According to Cook and Wyllie's *Street Directory* of 1903 the Consulting Physician that year was D McFadyen of 1 Park Avenue, Stirling, supported by Acting Medical Officers P B McNicol and W A Mackintosh, both local GPs, and Assistant Medical Officers J H Murray and E Moorhouse, also local Stirling GPs. The Infirmary's House Surgeon was J W Duffus.

One addition to the usual medical staff was the introduction of a consulting dental surgeon at the hospital – the first was Leon Jablonski Platt, author of *A Domestic Guide to a Good set of Teeth*, published in 1862 and celebrated in a later article by Stirling dentist Douglas Herd as 'the maestro of Murray Place'. His practice still exists in Stirling under the name of Platt and Common (Keith Common became his assistant in 1892). Platt retired from his practice around 1902 at the age of 62 but he continued for several more years as a consultant to the Infirmary.

Miss Peebles also believed in hard work. As one nurse (then a 'scared and shivering probationer') recalled later, her advice was that 'it was elbow grease, not bees' wax, that polished window sills', and that 'the way to get through your work was to go straight on from one job to the next, and not waste time in between'. In this respect, Miss Peebles was quite typical of all matrons of that time – Stirling did not suffer from an exceptionally strict or draconian matron.

In 1902 adverts appeared in the local newspapers seeking householders who would be willing to board convalescent patients from the hospital. The idea, apparently suggested by Miss Peebles, was very successful but it did expose the need for proper convalescent facilities in the Stirling area, for at that time there were none.

In spite of the success of Miss Peebles' appeal, in October 1903 the directors began to consider the idea of establishing their own convalescent cottage hospital, and by 1904 a lovely piece of land had

This nice view of the Chartershall Convalescent Home was published by the Stirling Journal to mark its opening in July 1906. *Courtesy of Stirling Council Archives.*

been purchased beside the Bannock Burn about 800 yards upstream from the Chartershall Bridge. Plans were then prepared by local architect Ebeneezer Simpson and, with approval from the hospital's subscribers (just over £7,400 was raised), work quickly went ahead. The brick and joinery work was done by R Anderson and Sons, the slater was T Blair, the plumbers were J and J Duff, plasterwork was by Alexander Walls and the painting was done by William Carson and Sons – all of Stirling.

When completed, the building, standing in 2½ acres, provided accommodation for eight male and eight female patients, with separate doors at each end of the house. There were also two large sitting rooms, a dining hall, a Matron's room and servants' rooms. The eventual cost was just under £4,400 which left around £3,000 in a fund to maintain and run the home. At first the place was supervised by a Mr and Mrs Philip until the arrival of Miss Robertson, the first Matron.

The building, which it was decided to call the Victoria Memorial Convalescent Home, was opened on Saturday 28th July 1906 by the Duchess of Montrose. A gold key, previously displayed in the window of Messrs D Stewart and Son, jewellers in Port Street, was presented to the Duchess who used it to formally open the home.

Almost immediately it became clear that this was a valuable asset to the Infirmary. Convalescent patients who would otherwise have occupied beds in the hospital could now be moved to the quieter,

Miss Robertson, the first Matron at Chartershall. *Stirling Council Archives.*

airier and more rural surroundings of the home. By 1913 no fewer than 190 patients a year were being cared for at Chartershall. By 1923 this had increased to over 300 patients a year.

The provision of this convalescent home by the Infirmary clearly prompted Stirlingshire's county councillors to do the same for the use of patients across the wider local area. In 1903 Ebeneezer Simpson was commissioned to add a convalescent building to the Fever Hospital at Bannockburn (by then called simply the Bannockburn Hospital). This was completed and opened in 1906. At

The convalescent home at Chartershall a few years after opening, by which time the gardens had matured a little. *Courtesy of Stirling Council Archives.*

the same time the 'Stirling Combination Poorhouse and Lunatic Asylum' (as it was by then known) was in 1906 restructured by local architects McLuckie and Walker into the Orchard House Hospital. The enlarged hospital building was nevertheless still basically the poorhouse, and it continued to be used only by local paupers and the elderly.

While the provision of a convalescent home was a pleasing addition to the Infirmary's resources, it did not especially advance its clinical work. By 1904 the hospital staff had grown and now consisted of the House Surgeon (who earned £6 13s 4d per month, which was £80 a year), Matron (who earned £5 a month), a head nurse (on £2 10s a month, which was £30 a year) and five training nurses, who each earned £1 6s 8d a month, or £16 a year. There was also a cook, a house maid, two laundry maids, a ward maid and a porter (whose wages ranged from the cook on £1 13s 4d per month to the laundry maid on £1 3s 4d per month, to the porter on eighteen shillings (90pence) a week. It would seem that the nursing staff also worked very long hours – it was not until 1920 that Miss Peebles recommended that the probationer nurses should have a half-day off each week and a whole day once a month.

In 1906 the Infirmary acquired its first X-ray machine and on 6th August 1906 Dr Graham Skinner (one of the visiting physicians), was appointed 'operator in connection with the X-ray apparatus'. As the end of year report to the AGM put it:

> An installation of Rontgen Ray apparatus has been made during the past year, and has been placed under the charge of Dr Skinner. The installation has given much satisfaction to the Medical Officers. By its use the condition of fracture can be observed quickly and accurately, and much suffering obviated. A special donation of £20 towards the cost was made through our Secretary by an anonymous friend, to whom the thanks of the Directors are due.

An X-ray machine at that time would have cost around £50.

Unfortunately it cannot be said that this put Stirling Royal Infirmary at the cutting edge of medical technology. X-rays had been discovered by Wilhelm Roentgen at Worzburg, Germany, in 1895 and by 1896 Glasgow Royal Infirmary had already established one of the world's first radiology departments. By 1901 Glasgow was regularly X-raying patients to diagnose and treat a variety of illnesses and

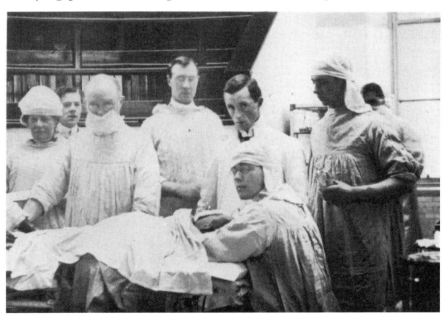

An early photograph of the Infirmary's operating theatre and its staff, probably taken in 1913. *Photo courtesy of the Stirling Observer*

injuries. Even at Falkirk Royal Infirmary a Dr Shanks had been appointed as anaesthetist in 1904, with the additional duties of supervising the ' . . . set of Rontgen Rays'. Nevertheless by 1906 the ability to make X-ray diagnoses had reached Stirling; later that year the directors' minutes record that 'Dr Skinner had taken a plate showing a needle in the hand of a lady. Afterwards an operation had been successfully performed.'

By now the local doctors who did rota turns at the Infirmary were more closely involved in advising the directors, and in recommending what they saw as the best ways forward. For example, in 1908 they asked for (and were given) a new operating table and a 'better way of sterilizing water'.

After 1900 Stirling's population began to expand rapidly, mainly because of new coal mines which were being opened in the area. The Polmaise 1 and 2 pits were sunk at Millhall, on the edge of Stirling, in 1902 while the Polmaise 3 and 4 pits at Fallin eventually went into production in 1906. With more pits expanding at Cowie, Plean and Bannockburn the centre of Stirling seemed to fill with large numbers of in-coming miners (Cook and Wylie's *Stirling Directory* for 1906 lists well over thirty miners, many with families, living in just Broad Street and St Mary's Wynd) until coal company housing could be built. In particular, there was very little housing at Millhall or Fallin until around 1907 by when the two collieries were employing almost 1000 men who lived in Stirling and walked out of town to work each day. One estimate says that the population of Stirling increased by 9,000 during these years.

By 1908 the burgh's average population density was 14 persons per acre but the 'top of the town' area (where these in-comers lived in hundreds of one or two-roomed dwellings) was 290 per acre. Similarly, Stirling's average death rate in 1908 was 19.5 per thousand, but Broad Street's death rate was 24.3 per thousand. Not surprisingly the Infirmary's workload began to grow as the population increased. In 1908 the hospital handled 391 in-patients and 2201 out-patients. Of these, about 35% of all patients received into the wards were coal miners.

As population pressure grew, the decision was eventually taken to enlarge the hospital yet again. At this time the hospital's capacity was supposed to be twenty-two beds but this was often increased by adding more beds down the middle of the wards. Of course this then led to a consequent concern about overcrowding

In 1910 an appeal went out to local people for the (approximately) £10,000 it would cost to build and maintain the proposed extension. Happily the appeal was very successful and around £12,000 was donated, some of it from local coal miners and colliery companies (notably the Alloa Coal Company, Archibald Russell Ltd. at Millhall and Fallin, and the Plean Colliery) who realised the importance of having such a hospital in the area, considering the exceptional dangers which miners faced underground. As the managing director of the Manor Powis mine said, the miners were 'combating against the forces of nature, very fickle, very unseen and very unrelenting'. In particular, many miners had already been treated for injuries caused especially by rock falls in tunnels, and might have died had the Infirmary not been available to them.

Apart from coal companies, additional money for the extension came from many other local sources including an increased number of local workers (for example the employees of the Caledonian Carpet Company), the Stirling Railwaymen's Charitable Association, local churches (such as the Greenloaning U.F. Church) and from the proceeds of 'Don Quixote', a comic opera held at the Albert Hall.

The enlarged hospital as it looked with its new side wings in 1913.
Courtesy Stirling Central Library

The new female ward taken from an old newspaper photo. *Courtesy Stirling Council Archives*

With the money now in place, plans were made by Ebeneezer Simpson for an extension to provide twenty-one more beds, a children's ward, separate anaesthetic and X-ray rooms, servants' rooms and even a hydraulic lift for stretchers and beds to the first floor. With the rear ground already substantially built over, the proposed extension could only be achieved by adding a new wing to the north side of the old bank building, vindicating the foresight and decision by the directors to purchase the derelict land there in the 1880s which allowed this expansion to be made.

In the end the north-west wing (closest to the High School) provided a new out-patients' waiting room, an out-patients' dressing room, a better dispensary, an X-ray room and a suite of rooms for the House Surgeon (all on the ground floor), with accommodation for twelve night and day nurses, a nurses' sitting room and sewing room, six servants' bedrooms, lavatories and a bathroom upstairs (and a fire escape stair to the rear). Meanwhile the wing on the east side seems to have been altered to provide an auxiliary 8-bed ward for men on the ground floor, with a 10-cot children's ward and toilet provision upstairs. The children's ward also had a large sun balcony to the rear and a fire escape.

As well as this, the previous wing built into the rear garden area was extended almost to the town wall, where it overlooked the Back Walk. It now included a 20-bed men's ward, a 2-bed acute ward and kitchens on the ground floor, and a 20-bed women's ward and other rooms upstairs. At the end of the wing were two square towers which housed bathrooms and toilets. In addition, the lower floor ended at French windows which opened out onto a large south-facing 'sun platform', while above was a sun balcony of the same size and a fire escape.

The interior of the original old bank building was also converted to include a Board Room and a hydraulic lift for stretchers or beds. The entire hospital now also had a 'system of interchange telephones', was entirely lit by electricity, and was entirely heated with hot water radiators – what a modern conversion!

For the record, the work was done almost entirely by Stirling firms. The mason work and arrangement of the grounds was done by R D and J Gardner, joiner work by Fairful, Wilson and Somers, plumbing by Robert Frater, glazing by Walls and Jamieson, slating and harling by A Oswald and sons, plaster and cement work by Robert Foster, electric lighting and telephones by Lockhart and McNab, painting by John Lamb, grates and mantles shared between Somerville and Valentine

The new children's ward taken from an old newspaper photo. *Stirling Council Archives*

and Graham and Morton, blinds installed by William Bain and leaded stair treads fitted by Virtue and Co. Beyond that the heating, ventilation, fire escape rails and balconies were all fitted by Mackenzie and Moncur of Edinburgh, the hydraulic lift was installed by A and P Steven of Glasgow, and the flooring joists and girders came from William Baird and Sons of Glasgow.

The new development eventually cost £4,800 (with another £5,000 expected to be required annually to maintain the extension and pay for the increase in staffing required). However it also gave the Infirmary a much improved 58-bed capacity, was built without causing a break in the regular work of the hospital, and allowed no fewer than 520 in-patients to be treated during the following year. The extension was opened on Friday 12th September 1913 by Sir David and Lady Erskine of Cardross. Lady Erskine also made a special opening of Children's Ward where she endowed a 'Lewis Carroll bed' in memory of the author of the children's book 'Alice in Wonderland'.

It was undoubtedly a great improvement. As one admiring description put it, '. . . the wards of the Infirmary are bright and sweet

The hospital staff, including Matron Miss Peebles, await the procession of King George V and Queen Mary, who visited Stirling in July 1914.
Photo courtesy Stirling Observer

and clean, with lovely flowers on the centre tables and on the patients' lockers, and with the kindly nurses in their pretty uniforms moving quietly about'.

And so the familiar frontage of the hospital, built very much in harmony with the older central part of the building, finally appeared as another landmark in the town. It is, of course, now the Colessio Hotel, but little do its passing residents of today know the stories of those passing residents who were the building's previous life.

Although the opening of the new hospital accommodation was probably the highlight of 1913, it was also a significant year in other ways. For example, the arrangement whereby six local doctors visited the hospital in a rota was changed to one in which just two (Dr P F McFarlan of Stirling and Dr Mitchell of Bridge of Allan) attended for the entire year, but were paid an honorarium 'in recognition of these services'.

In 1913 the first lady also became a director when Mrs McNab of Glebe Crescent was added to their number (so increasing the directors from fourteen to fifteen). This recognised the fact that most of the staff and patients at the hospital were female, that many of the subscribers were ladies, and that almost all the hospital's charity collectors were ladies, but at a time of Suffragette demands for the vote, it hardly challenged the dominant role which men still had in directing the hospital's affairs. Nevertheless Mrs McNab was gradually joined on the board by other ladies including Mrs Stirling, Miss McJannet and Miss Dundas of Laurelhill and the proportion of female directors did improve.

In August 1914 the First World War began and, as the government looked round for hospital and convalescent facilities for wounded men, life at Stirling Royal Infirmary inevitably had to change. The military authorities had powers to requisition virtually any building they felt necessary, and all across the area public and private buildings were soon taken over for all kinds of purposes. The Smith Art Gallery and Museum in Stirling became a cavalry store, St Ninian's School was taken over by the Royal Army Medical Corps, the Museum Hall at Bridge of Allan became an army billet and Keir House became a V.A.D hospital. At least three large houses in Bridge of Allan were requisitioned as either auxiliary hospitals, convalescent homes or nursing homes. Hyndwood Auxiliary Hospital, furnished and maintained by voluntary subscriptions in Bridge of Allan, eventually

Wounded soldiers convalescing in the Stirling area. From their uniforms the nurses seem to be Red Cross staff. *Courtesy Stirling Smith Art Gallery and Museum.*

treated 993 wounded men; a photograph of the Hyndwood staff shows the Matron (Mrs Milne Murray) and no fewer than thirty-four V.A.D and Red Cross nurses.

These treatment centres must surely have alleviated the numbers which would otherwise have been sent to the Stirling Royal Infirmary. Nevertheless, 2,615 servicemen were treated at the Infirmary during the war. To begin with they were Territorials, reserve soldiers hurriedly sent to France and thrown into the battles of 1914 and 1915. Those who 'copped a Blighty' (suffered injuries so serious that they would never fight again) were sent back to Britain for treatment and rehabilitation. Those with lesser wounds were normally treated in France and eventually returned to their regiments. 312 Territorials were admitted to the Infirmary between 1st November 1914 and 30th June 1915, although to start with they were mostly men who fell ill while still training at camps in the Stirling area (there were army camps at Forthside, Back o' Hill and Cornton).

Wounded soldiers were often brought home from France on ambulance trains, sometimes called 'convoys'. In September 1915 one such train, built by the Caledonian Railway Company to the order of the British War Office, spent two days on public display at Stirling station. Here, organised by the Countess of Mar and Kellie, people

Crowds gather round the Countess of Mar and Kellie to see the new Ambulance Train at Stirling Station in September 1915 (*Stirling Journal*). *Photo courtesy Stirling Council Archives.*

were allowed to inspect the train's carriages, known as 'ward cars', with their tiers of bunks down both sides of each coach. An impressive total of £775 was raised from the admission fees paid to enter these carriages, which was then presented to the Stirling branch of the Red Cross.

In his short history *Stirling Royal Infirmary 1874-1974* Dr W G Harrington quotes an interesting exchange of letters from this time. On 2nd February 1915 the (unnamed) mother of a soldier wrote a letter of complaint to Lord Kitchener, then the Minister for War, about the food at Stirling Royal Infirmary:

Dear Sir,

I take the liberty, perhaps the presumption, but it is an appeal and knowing you to be kind and a lover of justice it is on behalf of the Territorials which form part of your new army.

I trust I am not adding to your already numerous worries but I felt I must do something for enlightening and knew I could not go to a better source if this shall reach you as I hope it may, and if I have done no good then trust no harm.

Well, to begin, I had reason to go to Stirling Royal Infirmary this week to visit my only brother who had undergone a surgical operation for rupture. He joined the A.S.C. which is at Stirling.

I understand the Govt. has taken over one or two wards for cases of rupture, varicose veins and such like, all surgical. There are at present over 20 Territorials in one ward under treatment, and the matter which I wish to draw your kind attention to is the Bill of Fare which is so poor that the boys, I may say, for their ages range from 19 to 26 at the most. (*sic*). I went round to speak to a few of them to learn from everyone that if they were long in that place would come out more like skinned rabbits, and if they had known before joining would never have thought of it. I felt heart sorry, it was not the right spirit for the defenders of our Empire and I can't believe it is our Govt. to blame but the Town Council. Not being a proper military hospital, there is no inspection or questions asked if they have any complaint to make.

The Tommies are all growing and healthy and have good appetites for plain substantial food. I will give you an example of one day's Bill of Fare.

Breakfast	8 a.m.	4 tablespoons of porridge, more like gruel.
	9 a.m.	1 round of plain bread and margarine.
Dinner	1 p.m.	Small basin of thin soup, 2 potatoes and very small piece of meat.
Tea	4.30 p.m.	Tea, round of bread and margarine, no more One round is the limit.
Supper	8 p.m.	4 spoonfuls of porridge.
Lights out	8.30 p.m.	

Now, Hon. Sir, mind you, no complaint about dinner, only not enough by far. Of course, they don't expect beef or fowl, only plain and good. Two or three of them told me they were glad to smoke to allay the pangs of hunger.

What I cannot understand is how some hospitals give good food and others such as this so different and all under British Government. For instance, Stobhill Hospital, they are treated so different. Now if it is the Govt.'s orders then I beg to make my humble apologies for troubling you, but on the other hand I hope you will look into the matter for we all know the Empire has no use for weakling but strong boys and men.

I myself only a working man's wife with one of a family, [etc. etc...]

Not surprisingly Matron Peebles took strong exception to this criticism and wrote the following reply, which additionally offers an insight into the Infirmary's arrangements at this time:

I regret that Mrs. ... . has not furnished the name of her brother. If she had done so I would have been able to make a more direct investigation regarding this case. As, however, Mrs. ... . makes a general complaint, I may mention that many of the statements contained in her letter are not in accordance with fact. The bill of fare furnished by her is quite wrong. I enclose a copy of the dietary for perusal and I should like this to be sent to Colonel MacIntosh.

Mrs. ...... mentions that bread and *margarine* are included in the dietary. The Infirmary has never purchased one pennyworth of margarine. The best Danish butter is supplied to the patients at a very high price. We are fortunate in having an experienced cook at present and all the food is beautifully cooked. Fresh soup is made every day and it is wrong to call it thin soup. The men in the wards are happy and contented and many of them have thanked me very warmly before leaving for the care and attention which they have received while here. Several of them have spoken of the food supplied to the patients and have stated that it is above the average. They particularly referred to the soup and the porridge as of very good quality. One or two of the Directors of the Infirmary go round the wards every week when the patients have an opportunity of making any complaints either with reference to treatment or to the food supplied. No complaints have ever been made.

The patient referred to having had an operation for hernia would be under restricted diet for two or three days according to the Doctors' orders

During 1916 the first large-scale battles involving Lord Kitchener's keen volunteers of 1914 and 1915 began. The most obvious example was the Battle of the Somme which started on 1st July 1916, on which day the British army suffered 20,000 dead and 40,000 wounded – the worst losses ever suffered by the British Army in one day. From then on casualties from these horrific battlefields began to arrive at Stirling, just as at hundreds of other towns, mostly brought by hospital trains from the south of England. In August sixty soldiers with wounds too serious to be treated in France arrived in Stirling and marked the start of this grim phase in the hospital's story. During 1917 the hospital eventually treated 778 soldiers, and another 811 during 1918.

One sad case was that of 42 year old Private James Alexander of the 2nd/7th Battalion Argyll and Sutherland Highlanders. A married man from 48 Broad Street, he was wounded and brought back to Stirling where he died at the Infirmary just one month after the end of the war in December 1918. He lies in the Ballengeich cemetery.

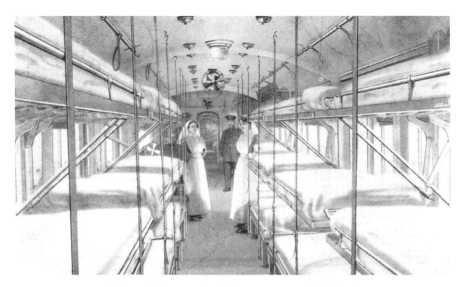

Interior of the Caledonian Ambulance Train, probably taken in 1915

All through the war the Infirmary tried to continue in its primary role as a centre for the local civilian population, while at the same time trying to provide as many beds as possible for military cases. It was a difficult balance to achieve. During 1916 the hospital dealt with 964 in-patients, of whom 128 were wounded soldiers, 218 were sick soldiers from units stationed in the Stirling area, and 618 were local civilian people. By 1917, however, this balance had changed – during that year there were 452 wounded soldiers, 326 sick soldiers from local army units and only 579 civilians.

As the hospital's annual report said at the end of 1917, 'The Infirmary is primarily a civilian hospital, and no suitable case from the civilian population is refused admission for the purpose of making room for military cases.' However the facts indicate the difficulty of adjusting to the additional strain of including military patients. By Christmas 1916 a 'recreation room' (actually a hut adjoining the male ward) had been provided for soldiers and was already supplied with games and books (mostly funded by the Duchess of Montrose or the Stirlingshire Red Cross Committee). Another X-ray machine was donated to the hospital by Mr and Mrs McGrigor of Beechwood. All signs of the demands of treating soldiers. Meanwhile the number of out-patient cases rose in 1917 to 1184, numbers at the Victoria Convalescent Home increased to 306, and annual expenditure for 1917 exceeded income by £871 (partly because the military authorities were so slow at paying for the treatment of soldiers, who were not, after all, sponsored by the hospital's subscribers, as civilian patients were).

By 1917 so many local doctors had either volunteered or had been conscripted into the army, there were only six GPs left in Stirling (which by then had a population of 21,000). In their place the Infirmary had to employ medical students for a fee of two guineas (£2 10p) per week. No record survives to indicate how well these students coped with the unusual demands now thrust upon them. However there was a nice moment when the Directors proposed altering the Infirmary's bye-law 7, which said that no child under six years of age could be admitted as an in-patient – a rule 'more honoured in the breach than in the observance' as the proposal noted, for in truth infants were already being admitted, even during those difficult wartime years.

For a time the war also distorted the typical pattern of illness in Stirling. With so many men away in the armed services the birth rate fell from 507 for 1915 to just 401 in 1918, which reduced (for a time) on-going demands that the Infirmary should include a Maternity Unit. There were also fewer cases of fever and, for a time, diphtheria cases were more numerous than scarlet fever. This was complicated, however, by twenty-two cases of malaria brought home by demobilised soldiers in 1919 and by the outbreak of influenza which swept Europe in the spring of 1918 and persisted until early 1919 (95 Stirling people died between July 1918 and March 1919 of flu and another 62 of either pneumonia or bronchitis linked to flu cases).

This pattern troubled the local Medical Officer of Health, Dr John McVail. Frustrated by having empty beds in some wards of the Combination Hospital at Kildean while having too many demands on other wards, and pressurised also by having an ever-increasing number of notifiable diseases to be isolated (for example polio, tuberculosis, malaria, cerebro-spinal fever, dysentery and 'pneumonia complicating influenza' were among those added to the list, and therefore to be isolated), he had a 'sectionalised pavilion' created at Kildean which allowed the hospital to receive and treat more types of infectious disease at the same time. On the other hand, there were no cases of smallpox in Stirling during 1915-1919, so that the Taylorton Hospital (and the County Smallpox Hospital which had been built next to it in 1914) was underused.

On top of all this there was no facility anywhere in Stirlingshire for the treatment of tuberculosis. In 1912 the Stirling Burgh Medical Officer of Health, Dr Wilson, pushed for the erection of a sanatorium to be paid for and run jointly by the County Councils of Clackmannan and Stirling and the Town Council of Stirling Burgh. During 1912 a suitable site was identified near the Barr Wood between Denny and Stirling, an architect was engaged to prepare plans for a 100 bed facility, and a government grant was made available towards the cost. But negotiations dragged on, the war broke out and the funding disappeared. When the plans were revived in 1919 the costs had increased beyond reach – no TB facility was ever built.

Meanwhile 293 serious cases of pulmonary tuberculosis were sent to sanatoria at Perth, Bridge of Weir, Lanarkshire and elsewhere between 1912 and 1919 (of whom 150 died). Additionally, between 1914 and 1919 a total of 193 non-pulmonary cases of TB were treated at the Stirling Royal Infirmary (of whom 44 died). Clearly the Infirmary was a busy place.

The First World War ended in November 1918 and from then on, through 1919, the hospital went through what its directors called 'a transition period' as it readjusted back to its normal life. During 1918 the Infirmary handled 822 military cases, which was more than half the total of all in-patients treated that year. During 1919 this fell to 244 and by 1920 it was only nineteen cases, mostly local disabled soldiers who needed further medical or surgical attention. Altogether the hospital treated 2,615 service personnel during the First World War – a record later inscribed on a bronze plaque displayed in the front hall.

In 1919 forty-seven local Voluntary Aid Detachment (VAD) nurses who had worked at the infirmary were presented with commemorative medals by the Duchess of Montrose in thanks for the part they had played in helping the hospital through the war years. Stirling's matron, Miss Peebles, was also highly commended for the way in which she had consistently managed to find enough nurses, and enough supplies (at a time of rationing), to keep the hospital running during the war. In May 1919 Miss Peebles was also awarded the Royal Red Cross by King George V at a ceremony held at Buckingham Palace for her 'Civil Nursing Service' during the war. It had certainly been a challenging time.

Nevertheless, the directors were now 'desirous to keep this institution abreast of the continual forward march of the Scottish infirmaries' and were looking to develop further. During 1920, for example, of the 998 in-patients, no fewer than 767 received treatment performed under general anaesthetic – an increase of 121 compared to 1919. That year the daily average number of in-patients was sixty-three – greater than at any time during the war. For this ever-growing work load Miss Peebles was paid £125 a year, with an additional allowance of £12 for her uniform.

There was also a strong wish to expand the infirmary. The British Red Cross Society was pressing strongly for a maternity unit, and was offering funds to help achieve this. Nurses' accommodation was also now very inadequate – six nurses were currently living in local boarding houses because of the lack of enough rooms. But following the extensions of 1913 there was simply no useable space left on the hospital site. At the AGM of 1921 the directors voiced this frustration and 'regretted the lack of accommodation, but now was not a suitable time for making an appeal for funds, nor for engaging in extensive building operations' (which, in a year of serious coal strikes and a post-war economic downturn, was probably true).

In spite of this, the Infirmary had by now received enough legacies, of varying amounts, to have accumulated an Endowment Fund of approximately £37,500. The interest from this added about £5,110 to the hospital's income, which was about 20% of the total required to run the Infirmary at that time. The directors were clearly still heavily dependent on voluntary subscriptions, but as this Endowment Fund slowly grew larger it gradually began to be known as the Building Fund – the first sign, perhaps, that another extension was somehow being considered.

It would be wrong to pass over 1921 without also referring to some other changes which occurred that year. During 1921 the directors lost Sir David Erskine of Cardross, their hard-working and influential President and Chairman of no fewer than 45 years, who died that year. He was replaced by Major A B Murray of Polmaise (who died in 1924). In the same year the hospital's treasurer Robert Cairns resigned after 40 years' service; at that year's AGM he was warmly thanked for the 'scrupulous care and constant attention' he had given to the finances of the Infirmary. He was followed in the post by Mr R K Anderson. Also in 1921 Sister Clark, deputy to Matron Peebles, left the hospital after twelve years to become Matron at the Ayr County Hospital.

In addition Dr Yellowlees, one of the visiting doctors, left for a position in Glasgow and was warmly thanked for the 'many calls on his time and strength so readily answered'. During his time the visiting doctors had also begun to give lectures to the nurses, so that they could pass the examinations required to be qualified for work in larger infirmaries. Along with Dr Mitchell, Dr Yellowlees was highly praised for his teaching skills.

In the same year the hospital's House Surgeon, Dr Ross, resigned after two years' work. From then on House Surgeons seem to have served just one year before moving on again. Over the next few years the quality of these surgeons seems to have varied – in one case the directors said that he had 'filled this office acceptably' while others had their 'valuable services' or 'constant and devoted attention, ungrudgingly bestowed on the patients' more fulsomely praised.

A lovely description of Christmas 1922 in the hospital has survived. As Christmas day approached, local ladies helped the nurses to 'garland with festoons of ivy and holly' the various wards. This greenery came from local estates, especially Polmaise, Blair Drummond, Touch and Steuarthall. In addition there was a Christmas tree in the children's ward from the Blair Drummond estate which was strung with electric lights (then still very much an unusual novelty), 'a blaze of light and shimmering beauty' contributed by local electrical firm Lockhart and McNab. Other tree decorations from Mr Craig of the Arcade 'added to the fairy-like aspect of the scene'.

On Christmas morning every patient then received gifts from many local well-wishers. For example, Mrs Murray of Polmaise sent pipes and tobacco for the men and beautiful cards and handkerchiefs for the female patients. From elsewhere came a pound of tea in a caddy for every female and mufflers and socks for the men.

The children were also 'kindly remembered, and when morning light came their eyes danced with delight at the stockings hung on their beds by Santa Claus, who had filled them with toys and sweets'. From Inverdarroch came children's clothing, and from other local families came dolls, crackers and other treats.

Breakfast on Christmas morning was another special treat and included fresh eggs sent from the Kerse Mill. Lunch included turkey, ham, plum pudding, jellies, fruits and 'crackers in abundance'. This was soon followed by an afternoon tea provided by Mrs Buntine of Torbrex House. After that there was an evening concert for the adult patients, organised by the tireless Miss Ethel Graham and which featured songs, violin and cello pieces and dancing.

At some point in the day 'the advent of Santa Claus, realistically impersonated by one of the Directors, created a joyful expectancy among the children, and there was a happy interlude when he presided over the distribution of gifts from the tree' (donated by the children of Allan's School, who also gave gifts to the hospital staff). After that the Allan's pupils entertained the patients with 'their delightful singing of some very beautiful carols', before joining the other guests for tea with Miss Peebles in the Board Room.

Considering that the patients were all from a poorer background, unable to afford private medicine and therefore requiring to be recommended by one of the subscribers, Christmas in the hospital must have been such a contrast to the poverty which they would otherwise have known, even during the festive season. It must have been an exceptional and memorable experience.

By 1924 the hospital staff had grown considerably from the eight medical staff and six support staff of 1904. The Infirmary now had the following:

Matron	Cook	2 ward maids
House Surgeon	18 nurses	Children's ward maid
Masseuse	2 nurses on trial	Out-Patient maid
Senior Sister	2 housemaids	Ward maid
Night Sister	1 nurses' maid	Porter
2 ward sisters	Laundry maid	
1 X-ray sister	Kitchen maid	

In 1874 when the Infirmary had first opened, the annual bill for salaries and wages was only £150. By 1924 this had risen to £2000.

Although the hospital's new extension had only opened in 1913, and the recent war had placed exceptional strain on the staff and buildings which perhaps masked the true picture, it is clear that by the 1920s the Infirmary was again facing considerable problems. One of these was overcrowding. By 1923 the Infirmary was receiving over 1000 in-patients a year, averaging over seventy a day in wards intended for fifty-six patients. With ward patients averaging twenty-four days in hospital there were now beds more or less permanently down the centre of most rooms.

In addition the original X-ray machine was 'obsolete and worn out' and a new one had to be bought. This cost an enormous £600 but 'the photographs obtained are almost instantaneous and very clear in detail. Local general practitioners can also have use of it on payment of certain fees.' The directors could have made lots of other improvements but they had to be careful with their expenditure, for this was the start of hard times in the British economy and the subscriptions which kept the hospital going could not necessarily be relied upon.

1924 was, of course, the hospital's Jubilee year. There was no great desire to spend foolishly on celebrations, but it is clear that the directors were determined to address the Infirmary's problems, especially the obvious lack of space which made it impossible to expand the building any further. From time to time hints had already been dropped. As early as 1922 one of the directors said, 'It is recognised that we will have to build one day, when the cost of materials and wages come down, but we have been putting off the evil day'. Nevertheless, by 1924 the Endowment Fund of legacies and bequests, (now more often being called the Building Fund), stood at £40,000.

Thereafter various authorities began increasingly to comment on the hospital's inadequacies. In 1922 a new clinic for 'special diseases' was established at the hospital by the Ministry of Health and the Stirling town and county councils. This was run by local physician Dr Angus and immediately began to grow. At the same time an ophthalmic department was started under Dr Pendleton White, a Glasgow eye specialist, and began to grow even more rapidly. It started with thirty patients but 351 were seen during 1926 and 587 during 1927. These new initiatives placed great strain on both available treatment rooms and staff. In addition, eight nurses were now boarding out for lack of enough living accommodation. On top of that, the Red Cross Association was still pressing for a maternity unit and the local Medical Officer of Health was lamenting the lack of any Ear, Nose and Throat unit, and was highly critical of the fact that 'nurses had to attend to surgical cases, medical cases, eye cases and sometimes noisy or delirious cases all in one ward'.

Having allowed the pressure of expert opinion to grow, the directors finally announced in November 1924 their proposal to build a completely new hospital 'whenever it is found possible to do so'. They proposed a 100-bed building with accommodation for 40-45 nurses, an out-patient department, new laundry, admission block, and other facilities of the most modern possible. The estimated cost was £65,000 to £70,000 but there was already over £56,000 in the Endowment

Fund (an extraordinary £9,793 having been bequeathed during 1923-24). They explained that other options were not viable – the existing site could not expand. Buying the site of the Girls' Industrial School next door would cost £40,000 and would, eventually, result in the same problem of a site which could not be expanded again. Meanwhile the children's ward was now too small, the laundry was out of date and inefficient, there was typically a list of forty people now waiting for in-patient treatment... and so on.

In support of the proposal Dr McFarlane, the Medical Officer of Health, pointed out that in an area of growing population (thanks largely to the thriving mining communities) there should be a proper fully-equipped hospital, centrally located. He also argued that there was a growing move towards 'decentralisation' and explained that 'the hospital work of a district like this should be done on the spot instead of sending patients many miles to the larger cities'. In addition there was, he said, a growing pattern of 'state' patients being referred to clinics or for surgery, many of whom needed prolonged treatment in wards, sometimes for over twelve months. There was also an increasing number of people being referred for tonsils and adenoids and '...these demands of the state will in future increase. We would like to be in a position to meet these demands'.

At both the hospital's AGM of subscribers in November 1924, and at a public meeting held in the Council Chambers of the Municipal Buildings, there was overwhelming support for the proposal to relocate the hospital to a new and larger site. And so planning towards a new building began in earnest.

During 1925 the directors purchased a site at Livilands for £5,200 and local architect James Millar (who lived nearly at Randolphfield) was engaged to make the plans. By now the anticipated cost had crept up to £70,000 - £80,000 and a new fund-raising appeal was launched, together with pictures of the proposed 126-bed building.

Even by 1924 (before plans for a new hospital had even been officially announced) the fundraising effort in Stirlingshire for a new building was an extraordinary example of community involvement. In July 1924, for example, local ex-servicemen held a fancy dress cycle parade and pageant in Dunblane. This included around thirty cyclists in fancy dress, around thirty street collectors, decorated charabancs, lorries and horses, Dunblane Pipe Band and the Bannockburn Colliery Brass Band, and raised over £50.

This view (probably from 1926) of the proposed new hospital was remarkably similar to the building which eventually opened in 1928.

By January 1925, by which time the scheme had been announced and serious fund-raising had begun, there were already 110 subscribers to the 'New Building Scheme'. With donations ranging from a few in the thousands to many of £1, the total in January was already over £20,000. By February it was up to £28,000 and by June 1925 it had reached over £47,000. By November 1925 the fund stood at over £52,000.

All over the area people did extraordinary things during 1925. In February a fund-raising whist drive was held in the Abbey Craig laundry at Causewayhead. In May the Millhall Pipe Band (who were at that time world champions) and the Millhall Male Voice Choir held an open-air concert in the King's Park. £47 came from a sale of work by the North Parish Church bible class. £731 15s 6d came in from the parishes of Kilmadock and Kincardine. The Stirling Co-operative Society held a 'mannequin parade' which raised £20. The Manor Powis Coal Company donated £500. A pony trot at St Ninians raised £80. A collection round the parishes of Dunblane and Lecropt produced donations from 161 people, while over £70 was raised from Doune residents. A collection round workers on the Coldoch farm estates raised £15, while another £11 came from farm workers on the Hill of Row. Staff at the Craigs School donated £16 10s, while the workers at the Skeoch Mill in Bannockburn donated another £20. A dance at Buchlyvie Public Hall raised £35. A Boys' Brigade march produced £2 5s. Stirling Amateur Swimming and Boating Club raised £40. A whist drive by employees of the Scottish General Omnibus Company raised more. A mothers' meeting in Dunblane donated ten shillings. Causewayhead Church Sabbath School raised over £10 on Easter Sunday. Employees at the Rockvale woollen spinning mill at the foot of the Craigs collected £24. The Bannockburn West Church Literary Club donated £4. And so it went on, for there were many more.

In spite of the General Strike and the much longer miners' strike of 1926, contributions kept coming in that year. By now building work had started, so there was something tangible to donate to. In February Lady Murray of Polmaise held an afternoon concert at Polmaise Castle. This was attended by 90 people in spite of the 'rough and wintry weather' that day. That summer a fete was held at Braco Castle, where General Sir Ian Hamilton (of First World War fame) mingled with ex-soldiers and raised over £350. In November the boundless Lady Murray staged an exhibition and sale in Edinburgh of her paintings. Opened by Viscount Younger of Leckie and called 'Flowers and Sunshine at Home and Abroad', it included ninety-seven paintings by Lady Murray herself, many of which featured secluded corners in the grounds of her home at Polmaise Castle.

Throughout this time the 'old' hospital continued to function as usual – indeed it became even busier as the ophthalmic unit especially handled a steadily growing number of out-patients. In May 1925 that year's provisions and services suppliers were announced. They included John Craig (greengrocer), John Duncan (chemist), Miss Johnstone (fishmonger), A T Paul (draper), D Somerville (ironmonger), D C Hardie (plumber), Wm Milne and Co. (slater), Richard Gordon (joiner) and Gilbert Henderson and Son (painter). In addition the Grampian Engineering Company at Causewayhead was appointed to repair a corroded disinfector at the hospital. This company specialised in making hospital sterilizing machines, which it manufactured until the 1940s.

At about this time the hospital also began to include Violet Ray therapy in its treatment. Popularised from around 1915 onwards but derided nowadays as little more than quackery, this apparatus enjoyed very widespread use at the time and portable models could even be bought for use at home. Sometimes called an 'ultra violet device', the makers claimed that an extraordinary variety of ailments could be alleviated, ranging from heart disease, paralysis, rheumatism, lumbago, cystitis, prostate troubles, venereal disease – even writers' cramp, skin blemishes, stiff necks and dandruff. Using radio energy from a coil and low-pressure gas electrodes, the device created a gentle warmth,

One of the hospital sterilisers manufactured by the Grampian Engineering works at
Causewayhead. These continued to be made there until the 1940s.
Picture courtesy of the Stirling Smith Art Gallery and Museum.

but also ozone and ultraviolet light, which were believed, not only to
effect many remedies, but also to stimulate the circulation and be
'effective for beauty, health and strength'. Ninety-four patients received
Violet Ray treatment during 1926 – the first of hundreds more.

There is no doubt that running the day to day life of the Infirmary,
but preparing also for the eventual move to a new building, was a
demanding and exhausting time for the matron, Miss Peebles, and in
early 1926 she announced her retirement. On Saturday 20th February
a farewell gathering of staff past and present was held in the Board
Room of the Infirmary to mark her twenty-five years' work as Matron.
After several speeches of reminiscence she was presented with a
beautiful dark walnut writing bureau, a stool and cushion, and an album
containing the names of eighty nurses who had served under her.

At a special public gathering held at the Municipal Buildings on
Monday 15th March she was additionally presented with a beautiful
case of cutlery, suitably inscribed, and a 'deposit receipt' for £266 12s
(more than twice her annual salary) subscribed by more than 650
well-wishers and former patients.

At the 1926 AGM Miss Peebles' work was again highly praised
when the Chairman (now ex-provost James Thomson) said that she:

. . . ungrudgingly gave the best years of her life to the service of the Infirmary. Her love of the work, and her genuine sympathy with the patients and their friends, have been the outstanding feature of her service, and these were the means of attracting a large measure of support from the public generally. The long-contained responsibilities and strain have, unfortunately, affected her health, but the directors trust that in rest and retirement she may be spared for many years in this district, in which she is so greatly respected, and where the memory of her services will not soon fade.

In March 1926 the Stirling Journal published this retirement portrait of Miss Peebles. *Courtesy Stirling Council Archives*

The hospital staff in 1926 taken on the steps of the Infirmary in Spittal Street. Retiring Matron Miss Peebles is seated in the centre of the front row. *Stirling Council Archives.*

Jane Peebles was replaced by Miss Isobel S Millar (from the Infirmary's own staff) as Matron. And so it fell to a new person to take the Infirmary forward to its new home.

CHAPTER FOUR

Miss Millar's Years

1926-1945

By 1926 progress on the new hospital was advancing. Ground at Livilands (described as 'between Livilands Bowling Club and Braehead Farm') had been purchased, and over £60,000 was in the Building Fund. In May the General Strike broke out across Britain and for a time work on the site was disrupted, but this was not too serious because real work on the site had not properly started yet.

The architect was James Miller (with Richard Gunn as chief assistant). Although he lived from 1911 at Randolphfield in Stirling (where he died in November 1947), Miller's office and practice in Blytheswood Square were very Glasgow centred and much of his work was in and around that city. Of the hundreds of commissions which he undertook, scores of them were for railway stations, including most on the Glasgow to Oban, Fort William and Mallaig west coast lines, but also including the lovely station at Wemyss Bay and the present Stirling Station (built in 1912). However, by the time Miller came to design the new Stirling infirmary he had also accumulated a varied and very interesting portfolio of other work, ranging from the interior of the SS Lusitania, the south stand at Hampden Park football ground and Partick Fire Station to the Peebles Hydro Hotel, the Allanwater Hotel at Bridge of Allan, the Savoy Music Hall in Glasgow, the Atholl Hotel at Pitlochry, Gleneagles Hotel, Turnberry Hotel, the Dunblane war memorial, and so on.

He also had some experience of hospitals, having designed the main building at Glasgow Royal Infirmary in 1901 and then many subsequent additions, and most of Perth Royal Infirmary, (including the maternity wing which he added in 1926). Although many of his buildings have been described as 'Glasgow neo-Baroque', Charles McKean in his architectural book *Stirling and the Trossachs* describes the infirmary at Stirling as 'a pleasant neo-Georgian block with projecting

The new hospital's Administration Block, photographed around
1960 but unchanged since its opening in 1928.

wings, tall chimney stacks at the gables, hipped roofs and plain
pilasters reaching through both storeys'. More importantly, unlike
some Stirling architecture of later decades, Miller's design has stood
the test of time as simply a 'nice building'.

In June 1926 contractors for the work were announced. They were
chosen by a combination of architect James Miller (who, perhaps, was
more familiar with Glasgow companies, where his office was) and the
directors of the Infirmary who were keen to use local firms, especially
at a time of slack work during the 1920s. In the end the contractors
were:

> Excavation, brick and mason work – John Patterson and Son Ltd., Glasgow
> Carpenters and joiners – William McPherson and Sons Ltd., Stirling
> Plumbers – Hugh Twaddle and Son, Glasgow
> Plasterers – Alex Walls and Sons, Stirling
> Painters – William McLaren, Stirling, and Messrs Ellery Brothers, Stirling
> Glaziers – Archibald Walls, Stirling and George G Kirk, Stirling
> Heating – Ashwell Nesbit and Co., Glasgow
> Fireproof floors – Messrs Thaw and Campbell, Glasgow
> Asphalt work – The Limmer Asphalt Company, Glasgow

Wall tile work –John Youden and Son, Glasgow
Terrazzo floor work – Messrs Toffolo, Jackson and Son, Glasgow
Lifts – John Bennie Ltd., Glasgow
Electric lighting – Primrose and Primrose, Glasgow
Kitchen fittings – R and A Main, Falkirk
Laundry fittings – Bradford and Co., Manchester
Sterilising plants – James Slater and Co., London and J Gardner and Co.,
        Edinburgh
Steel work and fences – P and W McLellan, Glasgow
The Clerk of Works was Mr William McIntosh, Tullibody

With this announcement work began immediately. Each contract included a time limit within which that section of work had to be completed, but in fact progress was remarkably rapid. Although the General Strike ended quite quickly, the miners continued into what became a long and bitter struggle which, with 6,000 miners out on strike in the local pit villages, did not end until November. It was not a good time to press a fund-raising effort (indeed, with mining subscriptions down during the strike, even the regular income needed to run the hospital fell in 1926 from £8,000 to £7,790). In addition, by the end of 1926 the estimated cost had risen to £100,000 and so a renewed fund-raising campaign was launched in 1927.

Once again a wonderful community effort began, as all over the county people rallied to the hospital's support. In March, for example, a whist drive and auction sale were held in Ashfield village hall and raised over £32. In May a display of dancing was given by pupils of Miss Ella A Blair in the Albert Hall. And there were many more events.

On Saturday 16th October students from all over central Scotland held their annual Carnival Day in Stirling, in what was an extraordinary effort of planning, local involvement and energy. At least 250 student street collectors, all in fancy dress, raised £346. Then they staged a procession through the town which included two fire engines from the Stirling Fire Brigade, lorry floats loaned by many local firms such as the Abbey Craig Laundry, Graham and Morton's shop, Scottish Oils and others, and also a motor car disguised as a submarine – this must have had an open top for there was even a conning tower from which a girl dressed in sailor costume rattled a collection tin. As well as this, a 'lorry sale' was staged at the top of Thistle Street where meat, donated by local shopkeepers, was sold literally 'off the back of a lorry' to raise another £41.

That evening the students then held a Carnival Ball in the Albert Hall. Five hundred people danced to Miss Sedgwick's Zingari Orchestra. The following evening Miss Sedgwick's musicians then held a concert at the Picture House in Orchard Place, which raised yet another £15. A great effort, but typical of the public attitude to the new hospital work.

During 1927 agreement was finally reached between the Scottish Board of Health, the local Child Welfare Committee, Stirling Town Council, Stirling County Council, and the burghs of Denny and Bridge of Allan to add a maternity home to the hospital. This would cost about £13,000 more but it would provide at least twenty beds (ten for the burgh of Stirling and the others for the surrounding county). The maternity unit would be linked to the main hospital building by a corridor and control of everything from furnishings, equipment and food to staffing and salaries would be added to the roll of the directors. Stirling Town Council would contribute to the running costs by paying a subsidy of six shillings (30p) per patient but local doctors would also be allowed to admit private patients provided there were enough beds beyond those for the 'certified patients' sent by the Medical Officer of Health.

Soon architect James Miller had added the maternity block to his plans and the building work pressed on.

Meanwhile work in the 'old' hospital continued as usual. During 1927 a total of 1,146 in-patients and 2,254 out-patients were treated, of whom 805 were X-rayed and 94 received Violet Ray treatment. The average stay in a bed was twenty-two days and the daily cost per patient was 5s 11d (almost 30p). The staff included house surgeon Dr Jack, ophthalmologist Dr John Pendelton White and chemist Mr William Yule. Local visiting doctors included Dr Alex McLennan (who, for years, travelled regularly from his practice in Glasgow), local doctors P F McFarlan and W B G Angus, and the first mention of a female physician in Dr Eva Cairns (who, when she obtained her FRCSEd in 1929, was immediately appointed as obstetrician and gynaecologist at the new Stirling Royal Infirmary).

At the subscribers' AGM in November 1927 chairman of the board ex-provost James Thomson announced that £75,000 had now been raised from public donations. With an expected £9,500 from the sale of the old hospital building, £10,500 in grants for the maternity home from Stirling Town Council and County Council funds, and another

£2,000 from a fund in memory of the late Duke of Montrose, the total was expected to reach around £97,000 – still a tantalising £11,000 short of the latest estimate of cost. 'We are on the last lap,' said the chairman, calling for one last effort from the public.

That effort did, indeed, go on. In February 1928 there was a major concert in the Albert Hall, organised by local music teacher Miss Crouch. All over the area other events were held – a whist drive in Buchlyvie, a flag day in Bridge of Allan, Women's Rural Institute collection boxes at Whins of Milton, and many other similar initiatives.

One specific scheme was very unusual. In May 1928 the hospital's lady directors Mrs Monro of Auchenbowie and Mrs Mowbray of Easter Livilands launched a 'Princess Elizabeth cot' endowment appeal. At that time the present Queen Elizabeth, eldest daughter of the

The photograph of Princess Elizabeth, used to launch the cot endowment appeal of 1928. *Stirling Council Archives.*

Duke and Duchess of York, was a two year old princess with a big mop of lovely golden hair so, under a delightful photo of the little royal princess published in the local papers, an appeal was made to local ladies who shared the princess's names (Elizabeth Alexandra Mary) to help endow a cot at the hospital. The target was £600 but the idea worked and eventually over £800 was raised.

In July the directors, desperately keen that the new hospital should begin its working life 'unencumbered by debt' then announced their final fund-raising initiative. Any person donating at least £1,200 to the building fund would thereby endow and name a bed. Any person donating at least £5,000 would have an entire ward named after them.

By the summer of 1928 the new Infirmary was finished and ready. In July the local press was taken on a tour round the building. This is how the operating theatre was admiringly described in the *Stirling Journal*:

The operating theatre has a northern exposure with a steadier light than that which the south affords. With large windows of sheet glass, a reinforced glass roof, a floor of white terrazzo and walls painted with Eau de Neille, the theatre is beautifully proportioned and lightsome. The water tap fittings are a special feature – they are of cromium, (sic) an indestructible metal with a very close resemblance to burnished silver.

The *Stirling Observer* was so interested in the bed lifts, which could carry twelve hundredweight (1344 pounds, or 610 kg) and travelled at 70 feet per minute, that it devoted an entire article about them in one edition.

Writing in the 1970s Dr W G Harrington described the new hospital's surroundings thus:

Great care was taken making the grounds attractive – the rock garden in front of the Administrative Block was much admired by many visitors, as were the many beautiful trees and shrubs which lined the original drive. Alas the rock garden and most of the trees have now disappeared.

As the big opening day approached, arrangements were made for the nurses who would be allowed to attend. One nurse later described what happened:

Three weeks before, Matron met the staff and told us we had to wear black lisle stockings and white cotton gloves. The stockings were no problem, except for lack of cash – our salary was only three shillings [15p] a month. But white cotton gloves we would not obtain as no draper stocked them. However, someone to our great relief heard that they were stocked by undertakers! When the day came one nurse had on black silk stockings (she was sent back on duty).

The new Infirmary was opened on Friday 10th August 1928 by the Duke and Duchess of York (later King George VI and Queen Elizabeth) who drove down from Glamis Castle for the occasion. Their first stop was at the Albert Hall where they were both given the freedom of the burgh and presented with charters kept in two silver caskets designed for the occasion with celtic themes by James Banks, jeweller in Port Street. The Duke and Duchess were also made honourary members of the Guildry of Stirling in another ceremony dating back for many centuries in the town.

The royal couple then drove up to Stirling Castle where they were welcomed by the Earl of Mar and Kellie, Hereditary Keeper of the

A fine panoramic view of the new hospital building, ready for opening. Published by the *Stirling Journal* on 26th July 1928. *Courtesy Stirling Council Archives.*

Castle, before having lunch in the officers' mess (for the castle was then still the garrison headquarters of the Argyll and Sutherland Highlanders). Finally the royal car left the castle at 2.15 and drove through streets packed with thousands of people before reaching the hospital it 2.30pm.

Men of the 7th battalion Argyll and Sutherland Highlanders form a Guard of Honour at the Albert Hall as the Duke and Duchess of York arrive to be given the freedom of the burgh in August 1928. *Courtesy Stirling Council Archives.*

The ceremony was held in the open area in front of the administration block, on an overcast day. The Duke and Duchess's programme for the opening ceremony was as follows:

Inspection of the Guard of Honour (provided by men of the 7th battalion Argyll and Sutherland Highlanders, which was the Stirling area Territorial Army battalion), local members of the British Legion, nursing staff, Stirling VADs, the Girl Guides, Boy Scouts and Boys' Brigade.

'God Save the King' played by the band of the Scots Guards on the arrival of the royal party.

Singing of Psalm 100 to the tune 'Old Hundred'.

Prayer of dedication by the Rev. W Stevenson Stuart, minister of the East Parish Church.

Presentation of a bouquet by Miss Lucy McFarlan to the Duchess of York.

Short speech of welcome to the Duke and Duchess by the president of the Stirling Royal Infirmary, ex-provost Thomson, and presentation of a key of gold made by D and J Stewart, jewellers in Port Street, Stirling..

Address by the Duke of York and the formal opening of the new Infirmary.

Inspection by the Duke and Duchess of wards, the children's ward and the maternity home, accompanied by music outside from the band of the Scots Guards.

Presentation to the Duke and Duchess of the directors, the architect and several of the staff.

Planting of two chestnut trees by the Duke and Duchess to commemorate their visit.

'God Save the King' played by the band of the Scots Guards on the departure of the royal party.

In his address the Duke praised the fund-raising which had enabled the hospital to be built, describing it as 'a magnificent achievement speaking volumes for the high ideals and public spirit of the people of the district'.

As the royal couple toured the building and were introduced to various dignitaries and members of staff, the highlight was probably when they reached the Princess Elizabeth cot in the children's ward. Lying nicely presented in the cot was a dainty little silver quaich and silver spoon for Princess Elizabeth, and a beautifully bound book containing the names of all the local Elizabeths, Alexandras and Marys who had subscribed to the cot's endowment fund, which seemed genuinely to delight the Duchess.

Unusually, the entire ceremony was broadcast live on BBC radio. The very first outside broadcast had only been in 1923 (from the Covent Garden Opera House in London) and the first live outside sports broadcast (the England v Wales rugby union international match) was only in 1927, so there was still great novelty in a broadcast

STIRLING ROYAL INFIRMARY

A. *D-19 7 20.*

The PRESIDENT and the DIRECTORS request the honour
of the company of

Mrs   David B. Morris & Miss Morris

on the occasion of the Opening of the New Infirmary
Buildings at Livilands by Their Royal Highnesses the
DUKE and DUCHESS OF YORK, on Friday, the
10th August, at 2-30 p.m.

Invitation to the opening of the new Infirmary. *Courtesy Stirling Council Archives.*

Platform ...... A ....   Seats No. D 19 ∘ 20

STIRLING ROYAL INFIRMARY

Admit

Mrs D.B. & Miss Morris

to the Opening Ceremony of the New Infirmary Buildings
at Livilands, by Their Royal Highnesses the Duke and
Duchess of York, on Friday the 10th August, at 2.30 p.m.

Seatholders are requested to be within the Grounds not later than 2 o'clock, as the main
thoroughfare is to be closed for traffic from that hour.

*Note.—It is not possible to arrange for inspection of the New
Infirmary on the 10th August, but days for this will be fixed
later and will be duly advertised.*

Admission card to the opening of the new
Infirmary. This one, for Town Clerk D B Morris,
indicates exactly which section, row and seat has
been allocated. *Courtesy Stirling Council Archives.*

The golden key used by the
Duchess to open the hospital
on 10th August 1928. *Courtesy
Stirling Council Archives*

Crowds of subscribers and prominent people gathering outside the Administration Block for the opening ceremony on 10th August 1928. *Courtesy Stirling Council Archives.*

coming out of Stirling. Indeed there was an entire article in the *Stirling Journal* of 30th August on how the broadcast was done.

There is no doubt that the success of the scheme, to raise £108,000 during the depression years of the 1920s and to create a completely new hospital in Stirling, was a tremendous achievement by the board

The Duchess of York planting a chestnut tree to mark the opening of the new Infirmary. Her tree still survives, but the tree planted by the Duke of York later died and was secretly replaced. *Photo courtesy Stirling Council Archives.*

The same tree as it looked in April 2011. The commemorative
plaque (inset) is at the foot of the tree. *Photo Craig Mair*

of directors. The *Stirling Observer* called it 'a Herculean task, carried to
fruition in the face of doleful head-shaking and foreboding that the
scheme was too ambitious to succeed'.

There is one footnote to this royal event. The tree planted by the
Duke of York soon died – and, according to one nurse, was 'replaced
one night at midnight'. This may explain why only one of the two
trees now has a commemorative plaque beside it (although even this
has had to be retrieved, more than once, from the doctors' room). In
1974 Dr W G Harrington wrote that, although the rockeries and
gardens had, by the 1970s, mostly disappeared, the two trees were
still there and were continuing to provide many thousands of conkers
– perhaps even he did not realise that they were, alas, not all royal
conkers.

In November the 'big move' occurred when the entire 'old' hospital
was transferred to the new building. This must have been some event
(and some sight) but it does not seem to have been well recorded.
However the AGM later in the year, which reviewed the past year's
momentous events, was reported by the *Stirling Observer* and included
this description:

... [concerning] the removal of the patients from the Old Infirmary to the new one, the directors noted how bravely, and with such good will, the whole staff so heartily and ungrudgingly gave this additional service. For their careful and fatiguing work the directors desire to thank all the members of the staff. They also wish to thank the VADs, the Railway Ambulance Men and all who, in any kind way, so kindly and voluntarily assisted at this strenuous removal. How well it was all planned, and how expeditiously it was carried out, will be apparent from the fact that the removal began at 7.45 and at 12.30 the patients were in the wards and partaking of their first dinner in the new home.

One eye-witness account of the move has also survived. In 1974 Miss Catherine Burns wrote her recollections in the Stirling Nurses' League magazine:

Then at the beginning of November one Sister and four nurses and the Cook moved out to the Infirmary to prepare the wards for the transfer of the patients. We had a very busy time but I think the Cook had the hardest, trying to get the rust removed from the boilers.

For three weeks we had no locks on the doors and no clocks, and every day packages of linen and stores for the different wards were dumped at the Out-Patient Department. It was no fun pulling them along the corridors and upstairs – the lifts were not in use and we had no trolley.

At the end of November the 'Great Day' came. From Spittal Street went the Matron, one Assistant Matron/Theatre Sister, one OPD Sister, who did all the X-rays, one Night sister, one Ward sister, seventeen Nurses, four Maids, one Porter and forty-four Patients. The children, twelve in all, went in their cots in one of Graham & Morton's vans. All patients were in bed in their different wards by 9.30 am.

Then we went to our wards and by lunch time we might as well have been in the wards for months.

With the new Infirmary well settled in, the hospital's visiting hours were then published in the papers. They were:

Sunday: 2-3pm
Monday: 2-3pm
Wednesday: 6-7pm (adult wards only)
Thursday: 2-3pm (children's ward only)
Saturday: 4-5pm

Tuesday and Fridays are *not* visiting days.

Sadly the hospital also suffered its first burglary in November that year when drawers were ransacked and money was stolen from the nurses' home by someone who climbed up a drainpipe, crossed a flat roof and got in through an unlatched window.

The first Hogmanay to be celebrated by the staff and patients at the new Infirmary seems to have been a happy affair. With a Christmas tree already donated by Sir A K and Lady Muir of Blairdrummond and decorative holly from the estates of Ochtertyre, Laurelhill, Easter Livilands and Polmaise, the wards were already looking bright and cheerful. On New Year's Day 1929 the staff and patients then had an excellent dinner, and in the female ward the ladies later had an afternoon tea provided by Mrs Younger of Gartur, and roast lamb supplied by local butchers. In one ward there was a concert and dancing display organised by the grand-daughter of one of the patients.

On Thursday 14th February 1929 the Maternity Home was finally opened by Stirling's Provost Barker (the councils of Stirling burgh, Stirlingshire, and the burghs of Bridge of Allan and Denny had paid for most of its cost, and would pay for its maintenance for the first three years). In his speech Provost Barker said that:

> The condition prevailing not only in the slum houses but in the smaller houses of the town are such that it is hardly possible for common decency to prevail when the little incidents of life occur, and I believe that the Maternity Home will be of great benefit to people in these smaller houses.

In her speech Dr Catherine A Douglas from the Scottish Board of Health added that the Maternity Home would be important because the proportion of women dying in childbirth, for lack of good enough facilities, was much greater in Scotland than in England – some 622 women aged between 15 and 45 had died in Scotland during 1927 and 32 babies per 1,000 had died within the first month of life.

By December 1929 the Maternity Home at Stirling Royal Infirmary had already received 143 in-patients and 99 births had occurred. From then on the numbers simply kept on rising – during 1934-35 there were 386 maternity cases.

1929 was also the first complete year of activity for the main hospital. By December that year it had received 1,985 in-patients (an increase of 822 on 1928), 3,368 out-patients (up by 398 on 1928), and had dealt with 817 Ear, Nose and Throat patients, 481 ophthalmic cases, 3,775 massage or electrical treatments, 205 Violet Ray treatments and 996

X-rays. Consequently expenditure was up by 74% and, not surprisingly, income from subscriptions and donations was £2,367 less than required (whereas there had been a surplus of £440 over expenditure in 1928).

Although Britain went through a considerable economic depression during the 1930s (sometimes called the 'Hungry Thirties'), this did not seriously affect the Stirling area, which was not especially dependant on heavy industry except coal mining. There was no great upsurge of the illnesses associated with poverty but, with a larger hospital offering more beds and treatments, the number of patients nevertheless increased – not because more people were falling ill, but because there had always been more ill people than hospital beds.

During 1931 the Infirmary admitted 2,265 patients. The average length of stay was 21 days and, including the maternity unit, the average number of beds occupied during the year was 130 – so the place was usually almost full. In 1931 there were 1,753 operations performed, almost all under either general or spinal anaesthetic, 5,345 attendances for massage or electrical treatment (the term physiotherapy was not commonly used then), and 1,593 X-rays were taken.

Many of the X-rays were to help detect pulmonary tuberculosis. Even in 1931, X-rays could detect this disease before any physical signs became apparent. 130 new cases of TB attended the Tuberculosis Clinic in Baker Street during 1931 and many were then sent to the Infirmary for an X-ray. Of all the TB cases that year, nineteen died, mostly people with TB in the lungs. Although X-rays could help to detect TB, they could also help to diagnose between TB and other lung conditions such as tumours. When diagnosed at the Infirmary, twenty-three people were then admitted to the Combination Hospital at Kildean, but they could only be treated there provided no other more serious cases of infectious disease were subsequently admitted – in which case they would all have to be discharged in order to let just one infection case have the ward. Fortunately this did not happen during 1931 but it was not a satisfactory situation. The local area really needed a TB hospital too.

During 1931 there were also 3,588 out-patients at Stirling Royal Infirmary, but they attended the out-patient department 21,844 times. It is clear that, in the days before free medical care for all, some people depended on the hospital for the treatment which better off people could afford to receive at home.

It is also clear that the hospital was very busy, indeed already working virtually to capacity. As A J Campbell, the Burgh of Stirling's local Medical Officer of Health, wrote in late 1931:

> The General Hospital for the district is the Stirling Royal Infirmary. The area which it serves includes the Burgh of Stirling, the county of Stirling, and the Western District of Perthshire.
>
> There are 106 beds for general, medical, and surgical cases, and 20 beds for maternity cases. While there is, as a rule, no undue delay with regard to the admission of acute medical and surgical cases, non-urgent surgical cases may in some cases have to wait a period of two to three months.

By December 1934 the waiting list was 203 people. By December 1935 this was up to 220 people.

By the early 1930s the directors (and Stirling's town council) were becoming concerned that, as admissions increased year-on-year, a 'hospital complex', as one councillor called it, was developing in the local population. People who used to be hostile, or nervous, or indifferent to hospital treatment, or felt that it was beyond their means, now realised that it was there, on their doorstep, and were beginning to feel entitled to it.

Unfortunately increased demand caused increased costs but, as the economic Depression reached its peak in 1930s Britain, subscriptions did not keep up with expenditure. Every year during this period expenses outstripped income – 'Another Infirmary deficit. Decrease in income from donations reported' said the *Stirling Journal* in January 1936. And when donations fell, legacies tended to follow. 1933-34 saw £4,981 gained from legacies, but this fell to just £404 in 1934-35.

Of course there were fund-raising initiatives going on all the time – whist drives, concerts, socials and dances went on as always. In 1932, for example, they included a Ball at the Golden Lion hotel, and a 'mile of pennies' event. During the following years there were many other interesting occasions, such as a display of dancing given by pupils of Miss Emmie Porter at the Alhambra Theatre in the Arcade in 1935, a concert given at the Albert Hall in 1936 by the famous Newhaven Fisherwomen's Choir, a charity bowling match at Bridge of Allan in 1937, and the 'Shilling Fund' in which people were encouraged to donate one shilling (5p).

Towards the end of 1928 a radio set was also presented to the children's ward by members of the *Stirling Observer*'s Young Folk's

Miss Emmie Porter's dancing girls raise funds for the Infirmary in April 1935.
Published in the *Stirling Journal*, the dancers are, left to right, misses C P Dick, E M
Welsh, E Ferguson, C Lawrie, J Cullens and B Hamilton. *Stirling Council Archives.*

Corner, a regular feature in that newspaper. The idea for this was born
earlier in 1928 when Boer War hero Captain Sir Beachcroft Towse VC
received a visit from two close friends while on a long stay in hospital.
Eager to help relieve the monotony of his hospitalisation, they rigged
up a makeshift wireless set, earthed to a nearby radiator (the BBC had
started the world's first national broadcasts in November 1922). This
primitive radio transformed Towse's life and caused him to establish
a fund to provide radio sets in hospitals. This fund was officially
launched on Christmas Day 1929 by Winston Churchill who broadcast
an appeal live from his home at Chartwell with an emotional plea for
money to buy wireless sets. Happily the children of the *Stirling Observer*
were well ahead of Churchill's appeal for by then Stirling's patients
had already been enjoying their radio for over a year.

This first radio in the hospital, a 'modern 4-valve General Electric
wireless set' as the *Stirling Observer* described it, was installed, together
with a loudspeaker, by W and T Marshall, electrical engineers in the
Craigs – indeed it was such a sensation that the newspaper devoted
an entire article to it in October 1928.

From then on children continued to send their pocket money pennies to the *Stirling Observer*'s 'wireless fund' and were listed each week in the Young Folks' Corner just like the adults who donated to the hospital's maintenance fund; a reliable radio cost around £2 in those days, which was more than many a man's weekly wage. By that Christmas this children's initiative had grown to the aim of providing radios in every ward.

From its first appearance in 1932 'Infirmary Week' quickly became one of the annual fundraising highlights of life in Stirling. During the chosen week, usually in May, there was always something for everybody, ranging from balls (usually in the Golden Lion Hotel) and 'midnight concerts' in the Regal Cinema, to visits by guest celebrities, charity football matches and a fancy dress parade through the town. In 1937 a football signed by all the players in that year's Scotland v England football match (which Scotland won by 3-1) was raffled. In 1938 the organisers even managed to persuade most of the best-known boxers in Scotland to put on a show in Stirling – they included British featherweight champion Johnny McGrory and walk-on roles for past legends Jake Kilrain and Frank Erne.

It must be remembered, however, that all this fundraising was just to keep the hospital running. During the Depression of the 1930s this was a constant struggle which never resulted in a surplus of income over expenditure – while income did increase most years, costs always rose by more.

To make matters worse for the directors, the British Medical Association suggested as early as 1930 that 'all persons treated in these [voluntary] hospitals, save destitutes, should pay according to their means', which was anathema to the directors and the philosophy of the hospital committee. This concern grew stronger when, at the AGM of 1932, guest speaker D P D Wilkie, Professor of Surgery at Edinburgh Royal Infirmary said:

> One other point which has been engaging my attention is the inspection of hospitals. This might not appeal to you in Stirling because an inspection is not required in your case, but the time has now come when medicine and surgery have become so de-centralised that inspectors have found operations being carried out in hundreds of unsatisfactory hospitals throughout the country.

It seemed that the trend of de-centralisation, which had favoured the building of local district hospitals like Stirling's, was now being

The 'Wailbirds' band ready on stage to entertain during the
Infirmary Week of 1934. *Courtesy Stirling Council Archives.*

Rob Roy visits Stirling's Infirmary Week in 1935 and is pictured
with some local supporters. *Courtesy Stirling Council Archives.*

'Prince of the Moslem Empire' Mustapha Koppa and his 'wives' arrive at Stirling
Station and set off into town for Infirmary Week 1935
Courtesy Stirling Smith Art Gallery and Museum

Girls from the staff of Marks and Spencers on their Infirmary Week
float of 1936. *Courtesy Stirling Council Archives.*

'Red Indians' arrive by canoe up the River Forth in time to take part in Stirling's Charity Week. *Courtesy Stirling Smith Art Gallery and Museum*

questioned – indeed even the local Medical Officers of Health were now suggesting that many smaller local hospitals should be rationalised, merged and closed. As early as 1931 it was recommended that infectious disease provision should be concentrated at just Falkirk and Bannockburn (with the closure of hospitals at Kilsyth and Grangemouth and Stirling County Council's withdrawal from participation in the hospitals at Kildean and Lennox), at least as a long-term policy, so as to 'prevent the spending of money at the wrong places'.

In early 1933, as demand continued to grow and resources were stretched by insufficient income, a new 'Treatment Scheme' was introduced for local workers. This involved paying a regular weekly contribution of two pence towards a time when they might require hospital treatment (just as subscriptions were seen as an entitlement to hospital care, except that the Treatment Scheme was for the payees themselves, and not to nominate someone else for treatment). The directors estimated a potential 12,000 suitable workers in the Stirlingshire area and by the end of 1933 10,783 had joined the scheme, which brought in over £4,000 each year.

By 1933 it had also become very evident to the directors that the hospital was already not big enough to meet demand. As one frustrated director said in 1933:

> When the buildings were erected five years ago it was hoped that they would last without interruption of at any rate ten years. Unfortunately it became evident a year or so ago that if we are to give patients that really efficient treatment for which they are entitled, we had to re-model and extend the out-patient department with all its varied clinics, and we felt justified in doing that out of capital... We purposely did not make any appeal to the public because we felt that the times were unsuitable for that.

> I might mention that there is a much bigger project looming ahead. The surgical and ear, throat and nose (*sic*) departments' waiting lists are a good deal longer than we should like them to be... Unless things right themselves we shall have to face an extension of the surgical wards.

During 1933, for example, the ENT department dealt with 1,734 cases, the ophthalmic department had 1,525 cases and there were 1,486 X-rays. There was certainly a problem, but this was a time of severe economic recession and most plans were shelved – a surgical extension would have cost around £6,000 in 1933 and the consequent expansion of nursing accommodation would have cost another £2,000. Architect

An inter-war Stirling Observer photo of the staff at Bannockburn Hospital. The two central figures seated are Matron Miss Clark and the hospital's GP Dr Morrison.
Courtesy Bannockburn Community Website

James Miller did design an out-patient extension which opened in 1933 at a cost of £7,000, but the surgical problem (which continued to grow as the number of traffic accidents increased during the 1930s) went on for another twenty years because of the lack of funds, and then because of the outbreak of the Second World War.

Nevertheless there were some interesting initiatives during these Depression years. In 1933 Mrs Donaldson of Airthrey Castle started a 'Linen League' amongst local women. Its purpose was to support the hospital by donations of linen and other similar necessities – something from which many other hospitals already benefitted. With Mrs Buntine of Torbrex as President and Lady Muir of Blair Drummond as one of the vice-presidents, the scheme quickly took off. It worked like a snowball, with each subscribing member finding six others to join until there were 'linen league' supporters in WRI groups, Girl Guides, church guilds, Women's Bright Hour groups and so on all over Stirlingshire. By as early as March 1934 they had already gathered and donated to the hospital a truly extraordinary number of sheets, blankets, pillow cases, face cloths, dish towels, bath towels, hot water bottle covers, table cloths, napkins, tray cloths, dusters, cot blankets, night dresses and dressing gowns.

The 'Linen League' went on for many years. During 1935 its members contributed 2981 articles, but by 1938 this was up to 3610 and the effort continued even when war broke out in 1939 – in 1940 they collected 2664 articles, for example.

Another initiative was the annual collection of eggs, known in some years as 'Egg Week'. In 1934 the *Stirling Journal* printed this fairly typical appeal:

> Have you any eggs to spare for sick people whose health, even life, may depend upon the nourishing nature of the food they get in the next few weeks ? This is a searching question to which most people, always excepting those unfortunates who are out of work, will not be able to answer in the negative without an unfortunate twinge of conscience... [if you donate eggs] you will be amazed at the glow of contentment which this deed will send through you . .

The appeal clearly worked, for year after year Girl Guides, church guilds, Women's Rural Institutes, Sunday schools and many others rallied to the challenge and sent in their eggs – 1934's total was 25,466 eggs, 1935's was 29,314 and 1939's was 24,906. This collection went on even during the Second World War when many foodstuffs were rationed. From January 1940 eggs were rationed to just two per person per week, but in spite of this the appeal still raised 15,282 eggs in 1941, for example.

In the end, for all the talk of a new surgical unit or the desirability of an orthopaedic unit, there simply were not the funds to enable these improvements to happen. Nevertheless some developments did occur during these lean years. During 1935 a new X-ray machine was installed at a cost of £2,078. As Colonel J C Dundas of Ochtertyre reported at the following AGM, ' . . . during the past two or three years the technique of manufacture [of X-ray apparatus] has improved so enormously that they are now able to eliminate risk to the patient and to the staff'.

The proper training of nurses also progressed. By now visiting physicians were teaching nurses towards their State exams. During 1935, for example, sixteen nurses completed training at the Infirmary, eleven nurses passed their final exams, eight passed the Central Midwives Board exams and twenty-four nurses entered service in the hospital. In addition there was now the annual presentation of the Risk Gold Medal, originally presented by Mr John Risk of Carlton, Stirling, who was Convener of the Infirmary's House Committee. In 1935 this was won by Nurse K M Mackie, 'the most deserving nurse as shown by examination and high standard of work'. From then on the presentation of certificates and awards became an annual highlight in the life of the Infirmary.

By 1937 the board was even, according to a newspaper report of the AGM:

> . . . toying with the idea of improving the working conditions of nurses, a subject which involved a pretty big financial problem. He [Colonel Dundas] was not suggesting that conditions in the Infirmary were bad, but times and conditions changed.... Overtime was by no means a desirable alternative for the employment of additional staff – in the nursing profession overtime was a public danger. If a nurse was not fit to give of her best at the end of 48 hours, no amount of overtime payment was going to make her fit . .

By now the Infirmary had also begun to develop its blood transfusion capabilities. The identification of different blood groups, pioneered by Austrian physician Karl Landsteiner from around 1901 (and for which he won the Nobel Prize for Medicine in 1930), and then the development of blood anticoagulants, had already made transfusions possible even by the time of the First World War. By 1926 the British Red Cross had introduced the world's first blood transfusion service and by the 1930s 'blood banks' were already beginning to be known. Even before blood banks, however, most hospitals at least had a list of donors who could be contacted at short notice for a blood transfusion in the event of an emergency.

Stirling Royal Infirmary's blood transfusion arrangements were not yet quite so advanced, however – basically they involved a phone call to Stirling Castle, which was then still a garrison for soldiers of the Argyll and Sutherland Highlanders and from where suitable volunteers could always be found. One such case was admiringly reported in the *Stirling Journal* in January 1935:

> An urgent message was received by the Commander of the Depot at midnight on Friday; volunteers were asked for and in a short time a large number were hastening out to the Infirmary. Two privates were selected, R Glasgow and F Keith, and they each gave a pint of blood. They did not know who they were helping but that did not worry these gallant lads, whose only recompense is a few days' extra leave.

By 1938 the new Infirmary was already ten years old and had settled in well. Of course changes went on like a drip-feed, ever renewing and replenishing the hospital's daily life. That year, for example, the indefatigable fundraiser Mrs Buntine died (and left a very considerable legacy of £13,500 to the Infirmary and the Victoria Convalescent Home at Chartershall). Dr W McLennan, who had been consultant physician for the past ten years, and for which he had always worked for no reward, retired, and was replaced by Dr T Kay MacLachlan.

Christmas, on the other hand, tended to be a constant fixture of kindness, generosity and happiness. In 1938 the wards were entertained by Mr Adam's Glee Party, Miss Reid and Mr W Herbert (violinists), a party of Boy Scouts, a group of 'gypsies' from the Riverside School supervised by Miss Boyd, Miss Barber-Fleming's Glee Party, Mrs Colbeck and Mr Duthie (violinists) and Miss McFarlan's Glee Party. In addition a choir of eight older Girl Guides toured the wards singing Christmas carols, and on Boxing Day patients in the Children's Ward were entertained by pupils of the Moss School at Blair Drummond, under Miss Duncan.

Although the Second World War did not break out until September 1939, the Infirmary had also been involved in forward planning for the possibility of war. As early as 1937, perhaps prompted by the recent bombing on 26th April of the Spanish town of Guernica by German planes during the Spanish Civil War, the first local air raid precautions talks began. The hospital was involved in discussions with Stirling and Clackmannan county councils, Stirling and Falkirk town councils, the British Red Cross Society and the St Andrew's Ambulance Association in 'preparing a scheme for the defence of civilians in the area about the headwaters of the Forth'.

By 1939 the danger of war with Nazi Germany was now much greater. Emergency hutted accommodation for 200 beds was built in the hospital grounds near Westerlands Drive, while elsewhere seven completely new Emergency Services Hospitals were also hurriedly started in areas unlikely to be bombed (such as Peel Hospital near Galashiels and at Killearn, where there were huts for no fewer than 640 emergency beds by 1941).

Sadly no records survive of patients at Stirling wearing gas masks or sticky tape criss-crossing windows, but it is probable that at least

An air view of Stirling Royal Infirmary showing the emergency wartime hutted accommodation built in 1939. Although taken around 1960, the scene had not changed since those early wartime years.

some basic air raid precautions were put in place. According to Ian Scott's book *Touch Ane Touch A'* , which is a history of Falkirk Royal Infirmary:

> ... [at Falkirk] blackouts were constructed for ward windows, black paint applied liberally, sandbags brought in and brick screens erected to protect wards and operating theatres from blast.

Another sign of Stirling's planning was the opening of Airthrey Castle as a maternity hospital on 11th September 1939 under the Department of Health for Scotland's emergency Evacuation Scheme. Although under the Department of Health's authority, it was administered by Stirling County Council until 1st April 1946 when it was taken over properly by Stirling County Council and became a County Maternity Hospital. The castle was offered to the Department of Health by Mrs Donaldson, who continued to live there until May 1941. At first the castle contained twenty maternity beds but after Mrs Donaldson's departure the Department of Health took over the entire building and the number of beds was increased to forty.

To begin with most of the patients were evacuees from the Glasgow area. Since the Clyde towns were likely targets for German air raids, pregnant women were moved to Airthrey Castle two weeks before the expected birth and then kept there for around ten days after the birth before being sent home. It was an excellent arrangement by which the patients could enjoy the peace of the countryside, fresh air and the castle's excellent garden produce. Some women and several hundred children were also moved from the Clyde area as evacuees to Stirling and Bridge of Allan when the war began – indeed, the castle's very first patient was an evacuee from Glasgow who was admitted on 12th September 1939.

The first baby was born on 15th September 1939 to a Bridge of Allan woman who had been evacuated back to her family from her married home in England. The total number of wartime admissions (from opening on 11th September 1939 to 31st December 1945) was 2386, and 2246 babies were born. Forty of these were still born and there were three maternal deaths (probably caused by a mystery disease which spread through the hospital in March-April 1944). Fourteen sets of twins were born there during the war. How statistics must hide so many human stories!

By the end of 1939 many evacuees had gone home because the Glasgow area had not been bombed and they thought it was safe to return. However, in 1941 the dreadful bombing of Glasgow and towns on the lower Clyde began and a steady stream of patients resumed, and continued to the end of the war. Most of these people came from Clydebank (where out of 12,000 houses, only eight were left undamaged after the 'Clydebank Blitz'), but the hospital also received women from the Rosyth area (evacuated away from the naval base which was regarded as a likely German target) and some from the London blitz of 1941 and the later 'V-bombs' of 1944.

During the war there was no resident doctor at Airthrey Castle. Under the Matron, Miss Clark, it depended on Dr Eva Cairns from Stirling Royal Infirmary as its visiting obstetrician. Many nurses came and went during these years – by the end of 1945 Miss Clark was the only member of the original staff still there, although there was also one nurse who had joined in October 1939. There was also one nurse surviving from February 1941 and one sister from July 1941. Four of the domestic staff, plus the chauffeur and head gardener, also survived

Although taken in 2010, this view of Airthrey Castle is unchanged since its wartime days, and would have been the scene which first greeted expectant mothers as they arrived at the castle. *Photo courtesy Cara Stern, Canada*

from 1941. The Women's Land Army also helped in the garden up to the end of 1945.

In due course quite a few local houses, mostly large country mansions owned by families which had always shown great support for Stirling Royal Infirmary, were also turned into wartime hospitals. These included Blair Drummond Auxiliary Hospital, Stanley House Minor Ailments Hospital in Bridge of Allan, the Dunblane Auxiliary Hospital, Keir House Convalescent Hospital and the Touch Hospital which was located in Touch House – special paths were even laid in the grounds of Touch so that wheelchairs could be pushed around. These places tended to be for convalescing members of the armed forces.

Stirling Royal Infirmary itself dealt more with direct medical matters such as operations – when ready for recovery patients were moved to the Victoria Convalescent Home or to one of the other local recuperation centres. By the time of the AGM for 1940 (actually held in April 1941) the Chairman of the directors was saying, 'it must be obvious to everyone that the work of the Infirmary has been greatly increased during the past year due to war emergencies'. The hospital's blood transfusion service described 1940 as a 'strenuous year' and was calling for more volunteer donors – by 1943 it was needing 90 pints of blood a week.

By 1940 the hospital was treating, as well as all the regular local civilian sick, numerous wounded soldiers from the war (some evacuated from the fighting in Norway, or from the beaches of Dunkirk). Looking back on 1942 the annual report stated that 'No large convoy of wounded was admitted during 1941- 42' (suggesting that there *had* been convoys of wounded previously). By 1943 the report was saying 'fewer military cases', which again indicates that there had been some in previous years.

One sad but typical case was that of Corporal Archibald White of the Argyll and Sutherland Highlanders. Severely wounded and captured in Belgium in 1939, he was held at Stalag 23A hospital until repatriated by the Germans to Leith on the Swedish 'mercy' liner Drottningholm in November 1943. Although brought to Stirling Royal Infirmary for treatment he died there of his injuries on 9th July 1944.

Although the evidence is scarce (mainly a speech made in 1945 looking back over the hospital's war years), it seems that there were also German prisoners of war among the patients treated at Stirling.

There were several POW camps in the area, at Denny, Comrie, Aberfoyle and Dunning but also much closer to Stirling, at Abbey Craig Park at Causewayhead (250 Italian prisoners), at the newly-built St Mary's Primary School in the Raploch, and in the grounds of Westerton House in Bridge of Allan, which held 200 Germans who arrived in August 1946.

In addition some patients were also civilian air raid victims. The records do not specify from where, but it seems that some may have been from lower Clyde towns such as Clydebank and Dumbarton, especially after the devastating air raids of 1941. Some may also have come from London.

Fortunately there were very few air raid victims in the Stirling area. Although German planes often passed overhead, following the moonlit River Forth on their way to bomb Glasgow and the Clyde towns, only two bombs actually fell on Stirling. At 2.20 am on the morning of 20th July 1940 a single German bomber, possibly returning from an air raid on Abbotsinch Aerodrome at Renfrew, dropped two landmine bombs on Stirling. They fell on the eastern outskirts of the town, one in a field where it did no damage, but the other onto the King's Park football stadium at Forthbank, which was so badly damaged that the football club never recovered and went out of business (to be superseded by Stirling Albion FC in 1945). Two houses across the street from the stadium were also badly damaged and nine people had to be rescued from the debris by ARP men. Mr Hugh McColl, a Mrs Tetstall and a young boy were taken with injuries to the Infirmary for treatment – Stirling's only air raid casualties.

On the other hand, the Infirmary did treat quite a few victims of the blackout. All road vehicles had to have blue paper over their headlights, and so it was that Annie Morrison of the Upper Craigs became a typical hospital case when she was knocked down by a van in the darkness of a blacked-out January evening in 1940. Buses were a special hazard because people could hear them coming but, with their interior lights and destination board lights switched off, the temptation to step onto the street to try to see where the approaching bus was going sometimes led to accidents. A particularly sad case was the one-legged man who did so in Murray Place and, being unable to jump back out of the way as the bus arrived, was run over. He was taken to the Infirmary but was found to be dead on arrival.

The remains of King's Park football stadium following the German bombing of July 1940. People in houses across the road became the only local air raid casualties to be treated in Stirling Royal Infirmary. *Courtesy Stirling Smith Art Gallery and Museum*

As the war went on, an increasing number of local traffic accidents also seemed to involve army vehicles. As more troops, some British but many from Poland, gathered to train in central Scotland the number of military vehicles on local roads increased and the number of hospital casualties rose, which all added to the workload. In 1938 the Infirmary treated 2,663 in-patients and 26,374 out-patients – by 1940 this was up to 3,113 in-patients and 28,764 outpatients and by 1942 it was 3,448 in-patients and 33,330 out-patients. Another indicator of this additional strain is that average bed occupancy in the hospital rose from a fairly typical 130 per night in 1935 to a serious 192 in 1944.

In spite of all these pressures (or perhaps because of them), the fundraising effort went on all through the war. There were many other causes which also needed funds, not least the Red Cross, but local people always seemed to be out there rattling tins, collecting eggs or holding whist drives and dances for the hospital. Surviving film, shot by the Regal cinema manager James S Nairn, of the Charities Day hospital fundraiser in 1939 shows a brass band, a pipe band, numerous floats, the Stirling fire brigade standing by their fire engine and trailer, shots of people dressed as Russian peasants, the Charities Queen and her maids in a horse-drawn carriage, but also a banner which says 'Help the Infirmary Today – it may help you tomorrow'.

That film was shot in Stirling town centre, but there was also a hospital flag day in Drymen, a tea dance in Cowie, a children's party in Bannockburn, a fundraising dance in the Burghmuir Pavilion to the music of Abercrombie's Orchestra, and an amazing £2,250 raised by the area's ARP wardens to endow a bed and a cot.

At one ball held in the Golden Lion Hotel in April 1944 and hosted by Mrs Gourlay, wife of the town's provost, people danced to the Highland Light Infantry's dance band and then forked out £145 to bid for various auction lots of whisky, sherry and eggs donated by well-wishers (local wages were £3 to £4 for a 48-hour week at that time). Another £18 was raised by the staff of the Allan Park and Queens cinemas in Stirling when 160 people attended their annual staff function with Cannon's Dance Band in December 1944.

As well as all this, Infirmary Week continued to be held every year during the war. In spite of austerity, rationing and a host of other deserving causes crying out for support, Infirmary Week even increased its takings each year. The first wartime 'Week' was in January 1940 when local newspapers set the tone by proclaiming 'Big Charity Effort Despite the War'. Sure enough, in spite of transportation difficulties and the call-up of many helpers, the big fancy dress parade went ahead, concerts and dances were held, and 5,000 spectators turned up to watch an 'air raid wardens versus fire and police' charity football match at Forthbank stadium (which the ARP won by 5-3). The result was another £1,100 for the hospital. This amazing effort went on every year. In 1941 it included pony trots and a May Queen. By 1944 the Infirmary Week take had risen to £3,000. In 1945 it rose again to £3,830 thanks partly to an impromptu concert held on the back of a lorry in Station Road by newly-returned POWs.

Of course, the 'normal' life of the Infirmary also continued through these years. Christmases and Hogmanays continued to be celebrated with the patients – not as lavishly as before, but they still managed to decorate a tree and find a Santa every year, and usually had a film show for the children and out-patients.

Nurses' training also continued. Indeed, with an ever-increasing demand for qualified nurses during the war this part of the Infirmary's work was more important then ever. In 1940, for example, a total of ten girls passed their final nursing exams and an additional six passed the Central Midwives Board exams (although another twenty-six girls left during that year before completion of their courses, which may suggest that the rigour of their training was not lessened, just because of the demands of the war).

The annual nurses' garden fete also continued (as in July 1944 when the stalls, including a 'gypsy' fortune teller, were manned by nurses of all ranks ranging from Sisters to trainees). As well as being an important fund-raising event, the day was always a great time of fun and socialising for the nurses, a short escape from the normal pressures and demands of their work.

The total number of nurses serving at the hospital also increased. 46 'entered' the hospital in 1940, for example. As a result of the demand for more nurses' accommodation the Board eventually bought two local mansion houses – Brentham Park and the Dhunan. In 1947 plans for a proper addition to the nurses' accommodation were approved by Stirling Town Council, even at a time of great shortages of building materials, such was the desire to correct this inadequacy at the hospital. Unfortunately Government priorities for building supplies meant that it was several years before this was actually built.

Every year the number of people attending the various clinics also increased. ENT out-patients were 1,288 in 1940 and by 1942 had risen to 1,454. The X-ray department handled 3,952 cases in 1940 – a figure which rose to 5,346 in 1945. The same pattern occurred at the ophthalmic, physiotherapy and Violet Ray units – even the maternity unit's numbers increased from 519 in 1940 to 560 in 1941, to 608 in 1942.

In 1939 Colonel J C Dundas of Ochtertyre retired as President and Chairman of the hospital's directors, having held the post for eight years. He was succeeded by Dr Patrick F McFarlan, who had for many years been the Infirmary's visiting consultant surgeon and who now served in this new role to 1945. Even with a war going on, he could foresee the need for the hospital to expand when peace came and at his suggestion another eight acres of ground was purchased to the south of the hospital in April 1942, at a cost of £3,500. In due course it proved to be a very wise move – the new nurses' accommodation eventually went there.

Sadly Dr McFarlan died later that same year. Described as a 'brilliant surgeon', he had served as a visiting surgeon at Stirling from 1910 to 1938, and as Medical Superintendent following the move to Livilands in 1928. In 1940 he was appointed President of the Infirmary and in 1943 he received an OBE for his work at the hospital. Throughout this entire time he also ran, for 40 years, a medical practice in Stirling.

The European part of the Second World War ended with the surrender of Germany on 8th May 1945. Although fighting continued in the Far East until the surrender of Japan on 2nd September, there was nevertheless widespread

Dr Patrick F MacFarlan, one of Stirling Royal Infirmary's great long-serving doctors. *Stirling Council Archives*

celebration in Stirling on VE day. Sadly no record has survived to indicate how staff and patients greeted that day in the hospital.

Having steered the Infirmary through the trauma of moving to the new building, and then through the economic hardship of the 1930s, and then through the pressures of the war years, Miss Isobel Millar announced her decision to retire as Matron in June 1945. Having previously also served as a theatre sister at the Infirmary, her dedicated service, her fostering of an excellent

Miss Isobel Millar, Matron at Stirling Royal Infirmary 1926-1945. *Stirling Council Archives.*

atmosphere in the hospital, and her attention to detail (especially cleanliness) were warmly praised at a retiral function that summer. She was replaced as Matron by Miss Jean Ritchie.

The surrenders of Germany and Japan in 1945 may have marked the end of one great struggle, but for some of the Infirmary stalwarts a new struggle was just about to begin – the coming of the National Health Service.

CHAPTER FIVE

Miss Ritchie's Years

1945-1966

As the post-war years began there were many matters at the Infirmary to be dealt with, but one dominated all the others. This was the new Labour government's intention to form a National Health Service. If carried out, it would end the voluntary status of the Infirmary and bring it under state control and management – an intention which seems to have brought shivers of deep concern to many at the hospital.

Of course this change was not a sudden new idea, forced on the country by the dogma of a Labour government. It was the culmination of answers to many different problems which hospitals like Stirling's had been facing for years – a perpetual tightness of funding, inadequate payment of nurses and doctors, the fact that some local people did not have access to its services, and so on.

As early as 1935 one guest speaker at the AGM had commented on the unique nature of the hospital service in the Stirling area – the cooperation which already existed between the local authorities and the management of the voluntary hospitals. 'You have carried out on a large scale an experiment which has been strikingly successful', said Dr R W Craig, the Scottish Secretary of the British Medical Association in his address to the subscribers and directors (appropriately, in the Municipal Chambers). His observations were correct. Ranging from their involvement in the various local fever hospitals to their support for the new maternity unit, the local town and county authorities had, indeed, developed a kind of cooperation between themselves and the voluntary hospital. Local Medical Officers of Health could now send patients to the hospital without a subscriber's letter. For a fee of just over seven shillings the Town Council could send maternity cases to the hospital. It was a start, the thin end of a wedge of 'state' involvement in the hospital.

At the same time there was also the Treatment Scheme, by which workers could pay tuppence (which eventually rose in 1944 to fourpence) a week towards medical treatment if it was ever required – not so very different from the eventual payment of National Insurance contributions by workers in the post-war years. So the mindset of the purely voluntary hospital of past decades had already begun to shift.

There was also the undeniable fact that, for years, the hospital's income from subscriptions and legacies had not matched its growing expenses, and so could it not develop its facilities. In 1935 the hospital's wage bill was £7,000 which, to those who could remember the smaller staff and salaries of the past, was now a serious challenge. In 1936 the AGM was quite bluntly told that 'assured income was inadequate' – a story repeated at every AGM thereafter until 1945. In 1939, for example, income was just under £20,000 but expenses were just over £23,000. And so for years an orthopaedic clinic and a nurses' preliminary training school, both much needed, could not be afforded and the hospital continued to rely on money raised by Infirmary Week and a host of other schemes, just to survive.

Then came the war, and the entire role of the hospital was forced to change as the government stepped in to use what resources the country had. The addition of emergency huts for the expected civilian victims of bombing became an example of the hospital's management surrendering its independence to the demands of the state. The Emergency Hospital Scheme became an early indicator, a practical demonstration, of what the regional coordination of hospitals might mean. Partly it would mean voluntary hospitals like those at Falkirk and Stirling losing some of their decision-making independence, but in return they would receive state funding to help compensate for the additional cost of wages and resources. Stirling Royal Infirmary was paid a grant of £23,000 in 1944, but then the question was, having grown to cope with the greater demands of the war years, with more doctors and many more nurses, would that money still be offered when peace came or would the hospital return to its smaller pre-war role?

By 1940 a great divide between the rich and poor of Britain had also been revealed by the war. The evacuation of people from inner-city slums to smaller towns and villages exposed a dreadful picture of poverty, malnutrition and disease in urban Britain. When Glasgow evacuee children arrived at Stirling in early September 1939 they were immediately marched from the station to the Orchard House hospital where they were washed with antiseptic carbolic soap and combed for head lice. One local councillor said, 'It has lifted the veil on the lives of thousands of the populace, disclosing squalor, disease, dirt and ignorance of the elementary laws of health and decent living that has appalled those of us who have had to cope with it . . .'.

It was a scene duplicated all across Britain, and became a problem which, even in the midst of war, the government could not ignore. As a result, Sir William Beveridge was commissioned by the wartime government to advise on how the country should be rebuilt when peace came. Beveridge had previously been associated with the introduction before the First World War of old age pensions and the first national insurance scheme, but he had been an economist since then. Nevertheless, if the social and poverty problems exposed by the war were to be solved, he was the right man for the job.

The Beveridge Report was published in 1942 and was an immediate sensation. It recommended that the government should find ways of fighting the five 'Giant Evils' of 'Want, Disease, Ignorance, Squalor and Idleness' and proposed widespread reform to the system of social welfare in Britain to address these. By 1943 these proposals had become a 'White Paper', a statement by the government of its intention to implement the proposals when the war was over. In a broadcast in March 1943 Prime Minister Winston Churchill described a four-year plan of reconstruction, and measures which would contain 'national compulsory insurance for all classes for all purposes from the cradle to the grave . . . a broadening field for State ownership and enterprise' including new housing, major reforms to education, and greatly increased health and welfare services.

There was overwhelming support for these proposals. Within two weeks of the report's publication in 1942 an opinion poll found that 95% of British people knew about it (even in those days before television) and wanted its recommendations to be implemented. A government survey also found the same thing – that the report had been 'welcomed with almost universal approval by people of all shades of opinion and by all sections of the community' and that it was seen as 'the first real attempt to put into practice the talk about a new world'. Looking back from today, it is certainly clear that the report gave people a goal to fight for, a vision of a new, better and fairer world to come after the war. As historian Geoffrey Rivett has written, health care was gradually being seen as a 'right, not something bestowed erratically by charity'.

At Stirling Royal Infirmary the White Paper was, of course, a great concern to the voluntary directors of the hospital, partly because it did not really make clear if the Infirmary would lose its independent status or not. And so at the Annual General Meetings of 1943 and 1944 there was much anxiety about what might lie ahead. Even by the AGM of 1945 (which was actually held in 1946, by which time the post-war Labour government had been elected and had already started to deal with Beveridge's 'Five Giants') the talk was still of concern about the coming National Health Service – 'the future organisation of the Hospital Service is still uncertain' said the Chairman, Sheriff R H Maconochie.

One major worry was that, 'swamped with a welter of forms and statutory rules and orders, the human touch will disappear', as one director said. Another was that local donations and endowments to the hospital would dry up. 'Money derived from them [contributions] may be spent on different hospitals and devoted to other purposes than those for which they were originally given or bequeathed with such local or sentimental affection', said Sheriff Maconochie in 1946, adding that 'popularly elected boards of managers will disappear and bureaucratic control by State-appointed committees, under the direction of a Government Department, will take their place'. It was a vision which he clearly did not relish.

This was again seen in 1948 when, speaking about the desperate need for more nurses, Sheriff Maconochie jibed that, 'It might be that the Minister of Health, who can do so many things, can make nurses – but I doubt it'.

The National Health Service (Scotland) Act 1947 came into effect in Scotland (under the authority of Arthur Woodburn, the Secretary of State for Scotland) on 5th July 1948. That day a four page buff coloured pamphlet was distributed throughout the country, explaining to the public what the new NHS was:

> It will provide you with all medical, dental and nursing care. Everyone – rich or poor, man woman or child – can use it or any part of it. There are no charges, except for a few special items. There are no insurance qualifications. But it is not a 'charity'. You are all paying for it, mainly as taxpayers, and it will relieve your money worries in time of illness.

Or as one cartoon character quipped some years later, 'Great thing about the NHS . . . a new hip won't cost you an arm and a leg!'.

Nevertheless, as the inevitable end of the Infirmary's voluntary subscription status approached, there were strong, sometimes bitter, feelings typified perhaps by those of the Chairman, Sheriff Maconochie himself. In 1947 he said:

> At this time, when changes of a fundamental nature are in the air, no-one can fail to visualise the future of the hospitals of this country with concern, tempered with the hope that order will emerge and that increased efficiency will result out of the ideals which have led to the inauguration of the National Health Service . . .

> But what of the attitude of the 'man in the street', who has been promised a 'new heaven and a new earth'? The government has not been able to deliver all the promises in the Bill for years, so when the public realises that things are going on much as before, I fear there will be grave dissatisfaction. The road will be long, difficult and full of pitfalls, and I think it would be wrong to allow the people to be under the misapprehension that a new Jerusalem can be built in a day.

The Infirmary came under State control on Saturday 5th July 1948. On that day it became part of the Western Region Hospital Board, to be run by the Board of Management of Stirling and Clackmannan Hospitals. They controlled all the hospitals around Stirling (those at Bannockburn, Kildean, Orchard House, Touch, Airthrey Castle, the Infirmary itself and also the Ochil Hills Sanatorium at Milnathort,), plus the two hospitals in Clackmannanshire at Alloa and Sauchie. Rather astutely, perhaps, the critical Sheriff Robert Maconochie, President and Chairman of the hospital's outgoing board of directors, was appointed Chairman of this new board of management.

Under the new Act the cost of running hospitals was to be met by the State and at long last the burden of dealing with the Infirmary's finances could be lifted from the shoulders of the indefatigable Captain E J McCutcheon who had served as both Treasurer and Secretary since 1928. In 1937 the cost per day, per patient, at Stirling had been 7s 9d (38p) but by 1947 it was up to 13s 6d (67p). By 1948 the Infirmary's deficit had grown to almost £45,000 – wiped out at a stroke by a government grant from the Department of Health.

Changes quickly followed. The Victoria Convalescent Home at Chartershall was sold for £2,900, but an enormous upgrading programme for hospitals also began. All over Britain there was a great surge to catch up with the maintenance and improvement which had not been possible during the war years. The emergency wartime huts at Stirling became a permanent fixture (and remained until 1992) but by late 1948 a new £10,000 X-ray department (described as 'the finest in the country') and an eye clinic were also under construction and plans for a new operating theatre, sterilizing room, and extension to the maternity home were announced, so it was an encouraging start.

As the voluntary hospital ended, its passing was marked by a dinner at the Allan Water Hotel in Bridge of Allan on Friday 25th June 1948. That evening the main toast was to 'The Directors of Stirling Royal Infirmary', but there was also acquiescence to the new. As one speaker said, '...there is an acceptance that the financial assistance of the State has become necessary. But it would be a tragedy if the sympathetic human touch, which has meant so much in the past, was to disappear in a welter of officialdom.'

In 1948 a 'Society of Friends of Stirling Royal Infirmary' was also formed, at the instigation of John Gray (a well-known seed merchant in Stirling) who lived in Gladstone

John Gray, a director at Stirling Royal Infirmary 1928-1948 and then founder and chairman of the Society of Friends of Stirling Royal Infirmary 1948-1971.

Place. At its first official meeting, held in the Municipal Buildings that September, he was elected its first President. The purpose of this society was to seek ways in which continued help could still be given to the Infirmary. Many people who had previously been subscribers to the old hospital joined the 'Friends' and subscribed in this way instead. Over the following years a long list of benefits was provided by the society, ranging from a tea trolley service and weekly visits to patients in the wards to the provision of books and the decoration of the wards at Christmas time. As a Friend said later, they provided the 'butter and jam which was the staff of life to patients in the hospital'. They even provided a pianist for the Sunday afternoon church services. As Dr Angus said in 1952 at a Friends fundraising function, 'The work of the Society helps to prevent us getting into the Civil Service attitude of patients having only numbers'.

And so the National Health Service began to take root in the Stirling area. By 1948 the number of out-patient attendances had risen from 2970 in 1928 to 40,848 just twenty years later – clearly the need was there. Nevertheless there were still feelings of both resentment and gloom among some. As late as 1950, when attending the Infirmary's annual prize-giving day for nurses, Sheriff Maconochie is reported by the *Stirling Journal* to have said that he was:

> . . . delighted to be there because it was one of the few places in this disgruntled world where he didn't see unhappy faces. Of course it was pretty difficult to be happy at the moment, with all the things that were happening around us, and also with the new Scheme which they were trying to work in hospitals. We had gone into the Scheme with bright hopes for the future of State hospitals, and everything was rosy. Everyone had been promised this and that, and there had been visions of a new heaven and a new earth, but no-one could say that these high hopes had actually been realised.
>
> However it must be remembered that the National Health Scheme was a very young one. We were cutting our baby teeth and the Scheme, he had not the slightest doubt, with considerable alterations (for these would have to be made by this or another government) would grow to fine maturity if we all kept in mind one or two things.
>
> We required to be unselfish and, under the National Health Scheme, that was very difficult because everyone was thinking not on their job, but on number one... Lastly, there must be determination to make the ruling Scheme a success, whether we got the bones to do it or not. It was being run in the interest of the patient, and one had to keep that before oneself all the time.

Of course, no matter who their political masters were, the staff of the Infirmary worked on as ever. This was reflected by Matron Miss Ritchie, who said in a speech in 1952:

> Someone said to me the other day that modern hospitals were so efficient you cannot even get a cup of tea unless it is your due. Well, so long as there is a hospital and nurses here in Stirling, there will be cups of tea.

In 1952 the *Stirling Observer*'s sports reporter Donald Cameron spent twelve days in Ward 6. While convalescing he wrote a very nice article in tribute to the nurses who treated him at the Infirmary:

> None who have ever been under the necessity of being in an infirmary ward for any length of time could fail to appreciate that the nurses must qualify

for being the most unselfish people of any profession in existence. Surrounded by rules and regulations which would compel strike action in any trade or industry in quick time, the girls and women carry on their duties in the most conscientious manner imaginable.

They have long hours of duty with a thousand and one things all wanting immediate attention. They never sit – even were they allowed to, it's questionable if they could find the time. And they remain unruffled in temper in the most exasperating circumstances.

Their income is tiny enough to compel them to lead a spartan life with little to spare for anything but the necessities of life . . . It would appear that the last thing they think about is the salary side of their job. The only conclusion which can be drawn is that they get all the satisfaction in the world out of seeing a good job well done.

The same could also have been said of the hospital's doctors. Because of the Second World War, when 'rank had been firmly established' (as one retired doctor said later) consultants still had great authority, to the extent that junior doctors were even expected to open their car door for them on arrival at the hospital. Nurses and junior doctors stood up when a consultant entered a room and everyone (except, perhaps, Matron) called them 'sir'. A junior doctor's working week could be as much as 120 hours on call, often doing two nights a week on top of their five days. They also routinely worked every second weekend so that their consultant seniors 'could stay in bed at night' as one retired doctor recalled. On the other hand, as 'apprentices' they learned by watching the skills of these consultants and in turn became experienced and highly trained themselves. As one retired consultant said, the working relationship with junior doctors and especially with the ward sisters, was 'one of the keystones of care' at Stirling in those days.

Although the State now paid for and ran the Infirmary, fundraising still continued every year through local dances, whist drives, gala days and other events. One such occasion was an evening held at Bannockburn Town Hall which included dancing by the pupils of Miss Mary Beattie and music from the Braemar Ladies Pipe Band. Even if the work of the Infirmary was now paid by the State, people ranging from church groups to the Stirling Post Office staff and the Stirling Albion supporters club still wanted to help provide the little extras which eased the life of patients and staff.

Sadly 1946 marked the last of the Infirmary Weeks. Whether this was out of a sense of relief that the hospital's finances would, in future, be on a better footing through government funding is not known, but the organisers certainly managed to go out in a blaze of fun and colour. Even in the grey days of post-war austerity they managed to stage a horse show, a charity football match, displays by brass and pipe bands, a barn dance at Cambusdrennie, a concert in the Kings Park bandstand and many other events. One of the most talked about was probably a ball held at the Golden Lion Hotel where a large crowd danced to the 1st Battalion Argyll and Sutherland Highlanders Dance Band. This evening also included an auction of rationed or hard-to-get things like bottles of whisky, sherry and eggs – someone even bid £4 (more than a week's wages) for the luxury of a bunch of bananas, which had been impossible to obtain during the war.

One happy moment came in September 1947 when the famous radio personality Howard Lockhart made a BBC radio broadcast from the hospital. The programme, on the BBC's Home Service, was called 'Appointment with Cheer' and offered 'mirth and music' from a

The happy group of hospital staff was snapped at a barn dance held at the Old Mill Farm, Raploch, in 1956. Funds raised at this event went towards the later provision of a recreation hall for the nurses. *Courtesy Stirling Council Archives.*

number of performers and the Scottish Variety Orchestra. There cannot be many occasions in the hospital's story when an entire 24-piece orchestra performed at Stirling Royal Infirmary !

Another important fundraising day was the Garden Fete held every July by the nursing staff in the hospital grounds, and which always attracted large crowds. With the flower beds and lawns beautifully prepared for the occasion, and stalls manned by all grades of nurses from Sisters to trainees, there was always something for everyone (usually including some nurse dressed as a gypsy fortune teller). The fete of 1956, for example, featured pony rides, a bottle stall, hand-knitted baby goods (made by patients and nurses), garden produce, cosmetics, a white elephant stall, ice cream, a 'mystery parcel' stall and even a crèche for little children complete with rocking horses. Even in the 1940s these fetes usually raised at least £300, which was a considerable sum at a time when nurses earned only a couple of pounds a week. By the 1950s the sum raised was usually well over £400.

Increasingly the money raised at these fetes went to particular nursing charities. One important cause was the Nurses' Benevolent Fund; elderly nurses did not have the benefit of National Insurance or superannuated pensions to support them, and so during the 1950s the newer state-employed nurses raised money for their older colleagues – a sale of work in 1951, a special nurses' reunion in 1952, a whist drive in 1953 and many more through the 1950s.

The front cover of the Stirling Royal Infirmary Nurses League magazine.
Magazine courtesy of Mary Ross

The benevolent fund was also supported by the hospital's Nurses' League. This was founded in 1948 to 'form a bond of fellowship between all nurses who have trained or held appointment at the Infirmary'. Although many nurses married and (as with female teachers) therefore had to leave their occupation, they continued to keep in touch by supporting the Nurses' League and holding fundraising functions all over the area – for a time there were annual whist drives at the Miners Welfare Hall at the Craigs, with prizes generously donated by local businesses to swell the Nurses' League funds.

There were also the annual staff dances, and these too invariably turned into fundraisers. These evenings, often attended by 200 or more people, were held at popular venues all over Stirling. The 1946 dance was at the Albert Hall, whereas the event in 1950 was held at the Plaza Ballroom. Led by Syd Kerr and the Plaza Orchestra, the evening included a hilarious performance of the song 'Dry Bones' during which a skeleton was used. The staff dance in 1952 was a masked ball at the Museum Hall in Bridge of Allan and raised money for a post-graduate nurses' training college in Scotland. On that occasion 300 people danced to music by the M.A.R.S. Band from Thornhill. The dance in 1954 was to music by the Bohemian Dance Band from Denny at the Golden Lion Hotel, while 1958 saw Jim MacLeod's Scottish Country Dance Band, also at the Golden Lion, and so on.

Prize winners posing outside the Administration Block in 1957. *Photo courtesy Mary Ross.*

Another important event was the annual nurses' prize-giving ceremony. This eventually became such an important day in the Stirling calendar that it generally gained a long description in the local papers, usually with a list of all the prize winners and often with a photograph of the assembled winners. The most coveted award was the gold medal presented to the 'nurse of the year'. The first time a male nurse received this medal was not until 1966 when 23 year old Bill Anderson was the winner.

Bill may have won the Risk gold medal, but he is also remembered nowadays as having been very much a prankster. Indeed, many of the stories of his exploits which he now tells are so outrageous as to be almost unbelievable.

For example, he says that, in typical student-prank style, he prepared for the prize-giving ceremony by glueing all the cups to the saucers before the guests' afternoon tea in the Recreation Hall and exchanging all the sugar for salt. During the night before, he says that he also decorated the trees in front of the Administration Block with bed pans and disposable urinals, which gave the porters a hectic time as they tried to remove them before the guests arrived.

By the 1950s the training of nurses and midwives at Stirling had grown considerably from the tentative beginnings of the 1890s. The Infirmary now had nurses at senior, junior and preliminary training levels. The prize-giving ceremony for 1952, for example, included awards to nurses at different stages of training for bacteriology, dietetics, venereal disease, surgical lectures, anaesthetic lectures, general nursing, ENT lectures, diseases of the eye, gynaecology and anatomy.

It was also a time when great changes were happening in medicine which nurses had to keep up with – for example, the first links between smoking and lung cancer were made in a report in 1950 to the British Medical Journal, and antibiotics such as penicillin, streptomycin and neomycin were beginning to be used widely as effective weapons against disease. There were also demographic changes – people were living longer. During the whole of 1947 the hospital treated just 96 patients who were aged over 60 but by 1952 this had increased to 140. In a sample of two randomly chosen wards on just one day in October 1954, thirteen of the thirty-two patients surveyed were over 60. It was a changing picture and nurses' training had to change with it. Nevertheless, any nurse who worked in the 1950s will still say that their most important training was simply learning on the ward from their more experienced seniors.

According to nurses of that time the three years of training which they received were rigorous (indeed one nurse described the first year of training as drudgery). Preliminary teaching was done at Moraig, a mansion house in Gladstone Place, once the home of W G Gardiner who had previously been Chairman of the old board of management. By the early 1950s Moraig had been converted to include a lecture room and a demonstration room fitted out like a hospital ward. There were also bedrooms where

W G Gardiner, Chairman of the Hospital Home Committee, who donated Moraig, his house in Gladstone Place, to become the teaching centre for Stirling's trainee nurses. *Photo courtesy Stirling Council Archives.*

up to twelve student nurses lived for their first three months, six girls sharing each room.

In the first year of teaching at Moraig the eight hour day involved lectures, demonstrations and practical work until five o'clock and then long spells of either cleaning or night duty, usually six nights on and two off. Preliminary instruction during the first three months included lessons in anatomy, physiology, hygiene, dietetics, cookery, first aid, bandaging and general nursing. This was followed by three months working in wards to practise the skills learned so far, followed by another three months of training, then back into the wards, and so on. Ward 13, which was a women's surgical ward in one of the wartime huts, was often used for the first three months of practical experience.

Girls could not start training until aged eighteen but the option to begin nursing as a career later in life was also there and women could start training even in their thirties. A student nurse was even paid the same as first year qualified nurses, which was a princely £225 per year, less £108 deductions. So she 'earned while she learned' as the *Stirling Observer* put it.

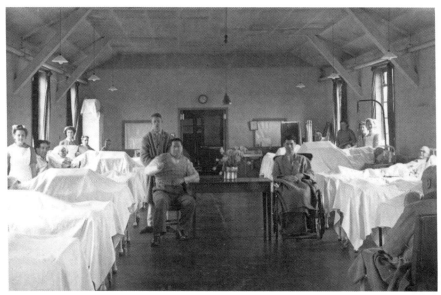

One of the wartime huts, used by the 1950s as a male ward for general surgical, ENT and road accident male patients (as indicated by the man with his arm in a plaster cast). *Photo courtesy Stirling Smith Art Gallery and Museum.*

Trainee nurses pose for the Stirling Observer's camera in 1953. They are from left to right: Margaret Neill, Sister Hume, Margaret Irwin, Chrissie Bell, Betty Brown, Irene Howatt, Mary Brown, Sister Wilkinson and Olive Gray. *Photo courtesy Mary Ross*

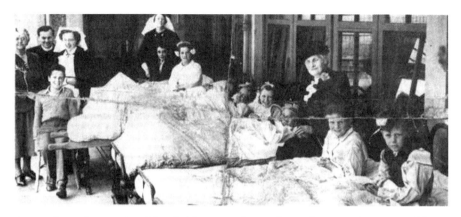

A rare photo from 1949 of the children's orthopaedic and TB ward at Bannockburn hospital. Matron Clark is standing by the door. *Bannockburn Community Website*

As the girls progressed they also had to do spells of work at the Bannockburn Hospital. They were told it was to gain experience of the scarlet fever, polio, dysentery, bone and spinal tuberculosis which was treated there, but the nurses believed it was because the hospital was short staffed and trainees were a convenient supply of labour. It is certainly true that there was a serious shortage of nurses, which remained a national problem right into the 1960s.

On the other hand, some nurses found the experience at Bannockburn fascinating and very different. By the 1950s this hospital had become the local centre for treating tuberculosis, dysentery and polio. The treatment of polio involved the use of an iron lung, an American invention of 1928 which placed a patient inside a full-length cylindrical air-tight steel tube which then acted as an artificial ventilator using air pressure. For a time, this was the standard way of treating polio until an effective vaccine was developed in 1956.

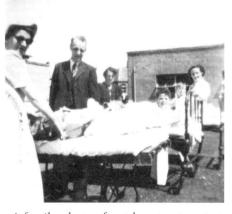

A family photo of outdoor treatment at Bannockburn from around 1950. The boy in the picture had a soft hip bone, for which he slept on a hard board for 18 months.
Photo courtesy Wilma Burns

The other common treatment at Bannockburn was fresh air. Some wards had entire end walls which could be opened, leading out onto verandas where beds were placed in the open air. Some patients were even required to sleep on the veranda, no matter what the weather was – even in snow. On the other hand, if trainees were sent to Bannockburn in summer, they usually returned to Moraig with a great suntan.

As they progressed further the trainees were given a Ward Chart, a little blue book (like a school jotter) in which a record was kept of their proficiency at things like giving injections (including mixing up their own penicillin in a teaspoon or preparing heroin on a Bunsen burner), sterilizing syringes, making up the instrument trays for operations, preparing the gauze dressings (which made their fingers raw), rolling up bandages and similar tasks. Much of this was expected to be done during hospital visiting hours.

There was an exam at the end of each course of lectures. These all had to be passed (only one re-sit was allowed) before a nurse could sit her final exam. With the completion of each year the nurse gained a white shoulder stripe which she put onto her pale blue uniform. When she eventually passed her final exams then she qualified as a staff nurse and received her new uniform that same day. This was grey coloured with a white pin stripe through it, but it also included the highly-prized starched white belt and cuffs, a gleaming white apron, and, above all, the frilly cap. As one lady recalls, she 'felt like the king of the castle' and went out to celebrate – leaving Sister McGuffie of Ward 3 to cope without her!

The graduation ceremony was held in the main lecture hall. On this day the nurses received the house badge which showed where they had trained – something to be treasured. They also received a certificate, although the fancy box tube, which looked impressive to the audience of admiring families, was often empty and the certificate would only arrive much later, once the paperwork had caught up. Later they would also receive a Registered General Nurse pin and a small round badge, at which point they could then register with the Royal College of Nursing (a registration which they had to repeat each year).

Although those who worked and studied hard usually graduated successfully, trainees were not always the angels they seemed to be. On one occasion in 1965 trainee nurse Bill Anderson claims to have responded to a dare by 'borrowing' a horse from neighbouring Braehead Farm (now swept away by a by-pass road) and riding it

Happy newly-qualified nurses in 1957, able at last to wear their Registered General Nurse pin. Back row left to right are: Jett McClugish, Esther Mathieson and Margaret Reid. Front row: Betty Brown, Margaret Irwin, Irene Howatt and Mary Brown. *Photo courtesy Mary Ross.*

through the main corridor of the hospital during one night-shift. Although it caused much entertainment for nurses and patients 'in the know', he was never betrayed or caught, and never disciplined. 'Only you would have done that!' smiled one senior nurse many years later, he says. If this is true Bill must surely be the only person ever to have ridden a horse through Stirling Royal Infirmary's corridors.

Encouraged by this success, Bill says he later organised three friends to help him one night to carry a donkey called Helen (also obtained from Braehead Farm) up a fire escape to Ward 1. Here it was tethered in the ward's sluice room where the light bulb was then removed. In due course Staff Nurse X visited the sluice room and, in the darkness, got the fright of her life. Having achieved what they had intended, the four pranksters then carried the donkey back down the fire escape and returned it to the farm. Another nurse from this time confirms the donkey story, and so it finds a place on the list of more unusual tales from the hospital's past. So much for nursing life at the Infirmary!

Although there were many changes for hospitals to adjust to after 1948, some pre-NHS traditions survived – above all, the role of the all-powerful hospital matron (and, to a lesser extent, the ward sisters). As the *Nursing Times* wrote in January 2008:

> These strong leaders were key to hospital nursing. As well as being impressive, one nurse remembers them as 'wonderful characters, big statuesque ladies who made their presence felt. They were scary but we could always go to them if we were in trouble'.

The 1950s Matron was in charge of all aspects of patient care, catering, laundry and cleaning, as well as staff homes and nurse training schools Even senior doctors would not dare enter a ward without first seeking matron or sister's approval.

Matron had tight control over nurses as Peter Ardern, nurse historian, says:

> In the 1950s, nursing was still traditional in terms of training and discipline. You still had Florence Nightingale values then and matron and sister had real authority. Matron then was as powerful as senior doctors. She had a bearing and an authority. Nurses living in nurse houses had to obey matron in their private life as well, taking instructions on how late they could stay out, how smartly dressed they were and the suitability of any young man they wished to marry – although getting married meant leaving the job.

In the recollection of nurses from that time, Stirling's Matron, Miss Jean Ritchie (or 'Jeannie' as she was called behind her back) was one of the strict brigade. Woe betide the Stirling nurse whose cuffs and collar were not starched properly, or who turned up for duty with incorrect uniform – nurses were not allowed to wear jewellery, watches or make-up in wards and their hair was not allowed to touch their collar (although they could tie it up in a bun). Even an engagement ring was forbidden, although they could pin it onto their uniform.

On the other hand, matrons could also have their own little weaknesses. According to some nurses Miss Ritchie had a habit of falling asleep in the bath and so would get nurses to wake her up by knocking loudly on the ceiling below – but, of course, nothing could ever be said, or even giggled at, when Miss Ritchie appeared. She also had a habit of sleeping in, so it was up to the nurses to be in the wards by 7.30 in the morning and have all the patients' names and diagnoses ready for Matron's eventual late arrival, often not until around 9 o'clock – but again, nothing was ever said.

There was also a breakfast gong which stood at the end of the corridor at Ward 7. Any nurse who arrived after the sounding of this gong would certainly be served last, could be summoned later by Miss Ritchie, and sometimes might not get any meal at all, in spite of the conspiracy of silence which they kept about the matron's own wee failings.

Occasionally the nurses retaliated. In 1967, for example, several of them (according to Bill Anderson) secretly emptied Miss Ritchie's office, lifted the carpet and placed stink bombs under it, then replaced the furniture and waited for events to unfold when Miss Ritchie next walked around her office. Although Matron could probably guess who the culprits were, she could not prove anything – the suppressed giggling at next morning's breakfast is still remembered (says Bill).

Sister Hislop (or 'Flower Power Maggie' as she was nicknamed in those hippie days) was also strict, especially about cleanliness. She often used to make the nurses polish all the chairs, but in return the nurses sometimes 'forgot' or had 'no time' to take the polish off and then had a chance to enjoy the patients' reaction to Miss Hislop.

On one occasion Miss Hislop decided to have a bath before going home. She started to run the water but then forgot about it while she washed her hair in the sink. Meanwhile the bath overflowed and water soon flowed under the door towards the X-ray department. Embarrassment, if not disaster, was only avoided by nurses who used hospital sheets and towels to mop up – but again, nothing was ever said directly to Sister Hislop.

Yet another of the strict brigade was Assistant Matron Marjory Donald. So on one occasion several nurses (according to Bill Anderson) took the wheels off her beloved mini car and carried it into the hospital kitchens, where they left it perched on top of the cookers. It required a major operation to have the car taken away again and reunited with its wheels, but the perpetrators were never caught.

Life for a young nurse at Stirling Royal Infirmary was very different from that of today. On paper nurses worked a 44 hour week but it was always more because many clearing up tasks had to be done after the official end of work. The working hours varied depending on the day but, in the recollection of nurses from that time, were typically something like this:

In a normal 44 hour week the nurses were given two mornings off, two afternoons and one evening, plus one entire day off and one half day on Sundays. Night shift was from 8.30pm to 7.30am, without any break.

For day nurses with the *morning* off, roll call was at 7.15am, when they were given tea and toast (they received no cooked meal until 12.30). They then worked from 7.30 to 9.00, when they got a break until 12.30.They had to be back for roll call at 12.30 when they received a quick cooked meal before starting work again at 1.00pm. This shift continued until 8.30pm.

For nurses with the *afternoon* off, they also had to be at roll call at 7.15 and then worked from 7.30am to 2.00pm. They had to be back on duty by 5.30 and worked through to 8.30pm.

For nurses with the *evening* off, their work ended at 5.30, but, in fact, the process of reporting at the end of the shift meant that they did not get away until at least 6.00pm.

Sunday was a half day and consisted of shifts from either 7.30am to 2pm or 2pm to 8.30pm.

Night nurses would arrive for duty at 8pm, followed by the appearance of the night sister on her ward visit at 10pm. By that time the night shift had to have learned the names of every patient in the ward, their diagnoses, and be able to report if any of those who had returned from the operating theatre had passed urine yet.

Nurses usually worked for at least three months on the same ward. Since patients usually stayed longer than they do in hospital today, this gave the nursing staff time to get to know the patients. However nurses only got warning of any change to another ward when they turned up for work that morning at 7.15. When that happened they had no choice but to move, no matter what bonds they had made with the patients in their previous ward. Night nurses could be deployed to any ward, as required.

On all days the main meal for day shift nurses was at 8.30pm. Sometimes they also had a later evening supper, which was usually deep fried triangular-cut bread and chicken fricassee.

Mealtimes in the dining room were very strict affairs. When the nurses entered they had to wait behind their chairs until the grace had been said by either Matron or the Assistant Matron. The tables were covered with green linoleum except for the Sisters, who had table cloths and napkins.

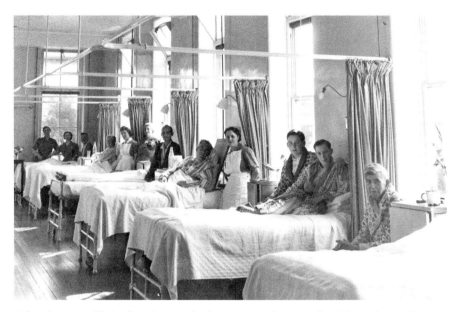

A lovely view of Ward 7 taken in the late 1950s. This was the old 'Nightingale' type of ward with rows of beds down each side of the room – very different from today.
Photo courtesy Mary Ross.

In the recollection of one nurse, 'The doctors ate somewhere else. Some of them could be aloof but some of the younger resident doctors did at least steal Jeannie Ritchie's bloomers once and hoisted them up the flagpole!'

When the meal was served there was a strict pecking order. Woe betide any nurse who was served before her seniors! There were no food options for nurses; vegetarian preferences, nut allergies, wheat intolerance and the many other food issues of today were unheard of back then. As one nurse said, 'With some foodstuffs still rationed until 1953 the girls had only two choices – take it or leave it!' One common dish which many nurses still remember, mainly because they hated it, was stewed liver.

On Sundays there was usually a roast joint. This was always ceremonially carved by Matron, but she took so long to do this that by the time the junior nurses received theirs the meat was often cold. Sunday dessert was usually rice and apricots, which were usually also cold. But whether it was cold meat, cold rice or lumpy porridge, the nurses dared not complain.

A 1950s photo of the female general surgery and urology Ward 5. The plaques on the wall recorded donors who had sponsored the beds in pre-NHS times.
Photo courtesy Stirling Smith Art Gallery and Museum.

On the morning of their final exams the nurses were given a special treat of French toast and sliced tomatoes for breakfast and steak pie for lunch.

The nurses' pay was low, but in Stirling they could get discounts on buses and in some shops (such as Boots) which helped. As one nurse said, 'These discounts saved us precious money, so if we were lucky at the end of the month we could sometimes afford to buy some No7 make-up'.

One great bonus for nurses was that, after qualifying as a staff nurse, they were allowed to 'live out' rather than be confined to the nurses' accommodation (which was locked at 10pm). This gave them a much greater degree of freedom and independence and as a result they often met the right man and got married.

This then led to the ritual of celebrating the engagement with her friends. As with factory lassies this meant being decorated and led through the town. In the case of Stirling's nurses it meant being conveyed in a wheelchair, with a bedpan on her head and her clothing covered with tissue hankie decoration, but at least it was only to the post box on Clifford Road rather than to the town centre where the embarrassment would have been greater.

Once married the nurse usually had to give one month's notice and then leave her career in nursing, at least until the late 1950s when the rules were relaxed because of the shortage of nurses. From then on married nurses were even allowed to wear their wedding ring at work, although married women were still not allowed to *enter* training as nurses. If a married nurse became pregnant she received only twelve weeks maternity leave (as was also common in many other occupations at that time). One nurse said, 'I worked until November and had my baby in December, but as I approached eight months they put me into the children's ward where there was less heavy lifting.'

The work of nurses was also very different from that of today. In the 1950s nursing involved much more hands-on bedside caring, and they had time to get to know their patients. Many patients feel that nurses today have to do a lot of technical work and paperwork, but have less time to take temperatures and tuck in sheets and generally fuss over patients. As one nurse said in 2011, 'these days we never have time to see our patients recover'. To nurses of an older generation, their days were like a golden age – strict, hard work, supervised by a hawk-eyed matron, but golden.

Matrons were one part of the 'triumvirate' which actually ran Stirling Royal Infirmary. Along with the Medical Superintendent and the Hospital Secretary (who, in those days, were all still medically-trained people with no qualifications in business management), Matron 'ran the place' as one doctor has said. These three decided how to spend the money given by the Health Board. According to some memories they also became especially skilled at playing Stirling off against Falkirk to the Health Board – 'how come you've given funds to Falkirk for a such-and-such?' was a common cry.

Beneath Matron were an Assistant Matron in charge of the domestic side of the hospital (cleaners, orderlies and so on) and a Home Sister who looked after the hospital's linen and the nurses' accommodation. Another important role was played by the Almoner who looked after the welfare of nurses and patients and dealt with cases of hardship. Many nurses remember Miss Melvin with great affection.

 During the 1950s there were many false hopes of improvements at the hospital. Nursing accommodation was an especially pressing need but shortages of money and building supplies seemed to put these good intentions always on hold. Even when local authority planning permission had been granted the Western Region Hospital Board or even the government could intervene to stop the plan.

On Tuesday 6th October 1955 (a 'red letter day' according to Sir Alexander Russell, Chairman of the Board of Management) a new 26-bed ward for the treatment of chest infections (and which cost £40,000) was opened at the Infirmary. The opening ceremony was performed by no less a person than Sheriff Maconochie (now Sir Robert Maconochie QC), the man once so opposed to the arrival of the NHS. In his speech he said that when he had been Chairman of the Board of Management they had eventually received permission from 'our lords and masters' to go beyond the mere planning, and now, some years later, here was the building completed:

> This building is a tribute to the National Health Service, and I never thought I would ever pay such a tribute to the National Health Service. It is a lasting memorial to the Welfare State, and I never thought I should say that either. It is a joy to the unwilling, over-taxed . . .
>
> Even the youngest of us can remember the day when consumption [tuberculosis] was a dreaded scourge from which there was little hope of recovery. The disease carried off tens of thousands. But miracles have now been performed and there is a completely different outlook, with much better treatment. Fresh air and hygiene play a large part in the success of coping with the trouble.

Dr Robert McIntyre, a future provost of Stirling who in 1945 had been the first ever Scottish Nationalist MP, but was now the chest doctor who would head this new TB unit, added:

> . . . There has been a recent and dramatic change in the treatment of tuberculosis. This is almost entirely due to the discovery of new drugs. Treatment is now finally effective for the vast majority of new patients. In 1953 and 1954 the death rate for Stirling County and Stirling Burgh fell to the astonishingly low level of seven per 100,000 of the population.

The building was designed by architect Graham Henderson of the Glasgow firm Keppie, Henderson and Gleave. Since its start in 1948 this firm had accumulated a strong portfolio of commercial buildings ranging from Glasgow biscuit factories to schools and banks, but they had also designed the Belford Hospital at Inverness, the Vale of Leven Hospital at Dumbarton, and additions to the Glasgow Cancer Hospital and the Clackmannan County Hospital, so they were a firm with a proven track record. The main contractor for the work was Messrs Duncan Stewart of Bonnybridge, the surveyors were James Barr and Sons of Glasgow and the Clerk of Works was Mr D L Inglis.

The plan for this unit differed radically from the old 'Nightingale wards' of the past, with their rows of beds down each side of the room. This had small rooms with between one and four beds in each, allowing greater privacy and also for males and females to be treated in the same ward. As the *Stirling Journal* reported, there was another new innovation:

> There is a system for signalling from the wards by patients by lights. When a button is pushed a light flashes in the nurses' room so that attention should be immediate.

In 1957 another improvement occurred when a new pharmacy building was opened, just inside the main entrance of the hospital. By now the old unit was too small to cope with the demands of all nine hospitals in the Stirling and Clackmannan Board area. The variety of drugs was increasing, and new methods of sterilising syringes by pressurised steam required more space. Disposable plastic syringes had never been heard of in those days.

Some nice stories have survived from the 1950s. Christmas 1953 was well remembered as the day when Dr Gilmour dressed up as Santa Claus and was an immediate hit in the children's ward. On Christmas Eve the off-duty nurses followed what had, by then, become a long-standing tradition at Stirling by going through the wards singing carols. On Christmas Day all patients who could walk were given their festive dinner at tables specially set up down the middle of the wards, so that bed-ridden patients would not feel left out. The turkey was usually provided by the Society of Friends and was always carved by one of the hospital surgeons. On Christmas night the off-duty nurses then put on an 'entertainment' organised by Mr Adam Lennox who had been doing this for many years.

In 1956 young Andrew Hamilton had a day to remember when the local Co-op store gave him a treat. Andrew suffered from polio but had recovered enough to play with his pals one day – only to fall and break his hip. Andrew was also a keen cinema-goer and was a member of the local ABC Minors Club. The movie craze at that time was the Walt Disney adventure film *Davy Crockett, King of the Wild Frontier* and every wee boy who could afford one was wearing a Davy Crockett hat, so when the Regal cinema management heard of Andrew's misfortune they approached the local Co-op outfitters department and had a Davy Crockett outfit made specially for the lad. This was presented in the

Ward 2, the Children's Ward, in the 1950s. *Courtesy Stirling Smith Art Gallery and Museum*

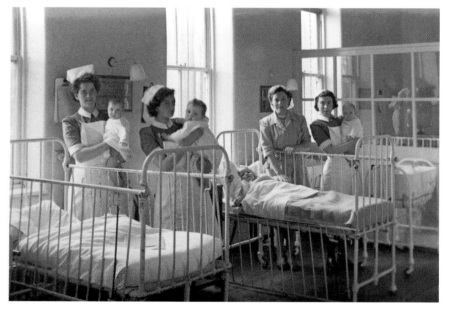

The near end of Ward 2 was for babies and infants shown here during the 1950s
Courtesy Stirling Smith Art Gallery and Museum

This happy group of children from Ward 2, past out-patient children, and
staff led by Sister Powrie was photographed at their Christmas party in the
Out-patients' Department in 1956. *Photo courtesy Mary Ross.*

ward by Mr Michael Kelly, local councillor but also chairman of the
Stirling Co-operative Society (and a future provost of Stirling), while
all the other children were also given sweets, Davy Crockett pictures
and balloons.

By 1960 the Infirmary was treating 6,500 in-patients a year – the
figure for 1947, the voluntary hospital's last year before the arrival of
the NHS, was 4133, which had seemed an enormous total at the time.
In the spring of 1960 another appeal went out for more blood donors
– now they needed 3,000 pints of blood a year (but were receiving less
than 1,000). It was a growing place.

That autumn the local Round Table organisation presented the
Infirmary with a telephone service in every ward – in fact this was two
phone sets on trolleys which could be wheeled into any ward and
plugged into sockets which had also been installed. At the time this
was an exciting innovation which the *Stirling Journal* said would provide:

... wonderful possibilities in sustaining the morale of patients, keeping them in touch with loved ones at home, and affording them the feeling that they are not entirely out of circulation... Of course the patient pays – there is the usual coin box attached to each instrument.

By this time some of the older names long associated with the Infirmary were beginning to disappear from the pages of its history. In 1954 Dr William B G Angus retired after a lifetime of service to the hospital which he had first joined as a visiting medical officer in 1921, having served as an army surgical specialist in the First World War. Thereafter he eventually became Senior Consultant Surgeon and retired as Medical Superintendent.

Dr William Angus, who served the Infirmary from 1921 to 1954. *Photo courtesy Stirling Council Archives.*

In 1960 Dr T Kay Maclachlan retired from the infirmary, having joined as a visiting physician in 1938. So severely wounded in the First World War that he was invalided out of the Argyll and Sutherland Highlanders, he spent a year in hospital before returning to Cambridge University, where he eventually graduated with an M.A., M.B,Ch.B. After working mostly in Glasgow hospitals for twenty years he finally moved to Stirling from where he retired as Consultant Physician in charge of the Medical Department.

One by one, people who had worked at the hospital in its pre-war days were leaving; the 'great generation' as consultant surgeon Dudley Booth called them recently.

By the 1960s the National Health Service had found its feet and was well established. The national economy was also growing and small improvements began to appear at the hospital. One of the most welcome was the opening of a nurses' Recreation Hall in May 1961. As early as 1957 the nurses had put the £475 raised at their annual fete towards the construction of a 'recreation hut' because they had been told that 'the Board is very keenly aware of this lack of facilities and it is only a lack of finance which has restricted them from doing anything'. Well in 1961 they finally got their 'hut'. As the *Stirling Journal* reported:

> The staff of Stirling Royal Infirmary have waited long and worked hard for a recreation hall and yesterday their dreams became a reality when a fine, modern, well-equipped and spacious hall was officially opened by Chairman of the regional Hospital Board, Mr A R Proctor.

The 'hut' was actually a fine function hall with a proper stage (including red curtains), a sitting room, kitchen facilities and toilets. In keeping with the trends of that time the décor included black and yellow floor tiles, and metal framed chairs and tables in a 'soft shade of blue'. From then on it was often used for dances, meetings, Burns Suppers and other events; one of the first was a coffee morning which raised £67 for the Scottish Nurses Benevolent Fund.

More improvements followed. In May 1961 a new Nurses Training Unit block was opened, at a cost of £16,000. By 1962 a new 22-bed Women's Diseases Ward was under construction above the single-storey children's ward (which also allowed the work of the hospital, even in the children's ward, to go on virtually uninterrupted). With improved medicines, better techniques and money to pay for more staff and better facilities, there was a feeling of great progress in the air.

In a speech at the time, Group Medical Superintendent Dr W G Harrington announced that this was the start of a long-term development programme which would eventually result in improved casualty, out-patient and visitor facilities. This new wing, with its air conditioned rooms and costing no less than £110,000, was eventually opened on Thursday 29th April 1965 by Sir James Younger. The biggest improvement was perhaps that casualties and normal visitors now had separate entrance doors, which reduced congestion and speeded up the arrival of emergency cases to their point of treatment. In 1964 Stirling Royal Infirmary had treated 99,570 out-patients, of whom 12,106 had attended the Casualty Department, so the need for better facilities was certainly clear.

Over the following years there was more talk of upgrading the hospital's facilities, but it was much longer before these intentions turned into bricks and mortar. In 1964 there were whispers of a wonderful new £53,000 X-ray unit which would combine with the hospitals at Falkirk, Clackmannan and Killearn and feature the latest

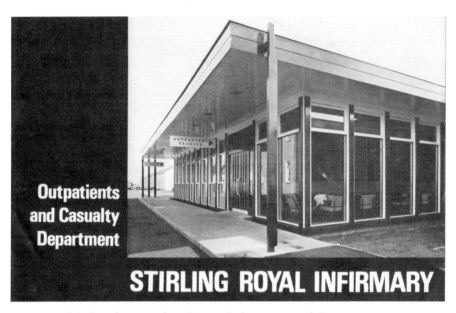

Cover of the brochure produced to mark the opening of the new Outpatients and Casualty departments in April 1965. *Brochure courtesy Margaret Plenderleith.*

apparatus, and which required a much lower radiation dosage to give an even sharper picture. Then in 1965 there were articles in the local papers about a new maternity unit which was to be built 'fairly soon'. By this time plans for a new university at Stirling had been announced, to be built on the Airthrey estate and to include the Airthrey Castle maternity hospital, so it was clear that a new maternity unit would, indeed, be required eventually – but not until 1969.

While the gradual expansion and improvement of hospital facilities was a feature of the 1960s, there were many other moments in its daily life which were also of interest. During the late 1950s and early 1960s the use of the sedative drug thalidomide resulted in the birth of at least 10,000 deformed babies in 46 countries; around 2,000 babies were born with defects in Britain, where the drug had been licensed in 1958. At a conference of women trades unionists held at Stirling's Albert Hall in 1962, high praise was given to the Infirmary's Dr A L Spiers for his 'promptitude in withdrawing the use of the thalidomide drug' at the hospital. Indeed, some Stirling staff believe that he may have been the first doctor in Britain to recognise the dangers of thalidomide and that the Infirmary may have been the first place to discontinue its use.

On a lighter note, on Saturday 19th September 1964 the first hospital broadcast by the Forth Radio Network service began at Stirling. Run by volunteers, this type of hospital radio had already been very successfully introduced at Edinburgh and Dunfermline and was brought to Stirling by the initiative of Dr W G Harrington. The programmes were mostly record request shows but also included news bulletins, interviews with local people and other items of local interest. Patients listened to the broadcasts through ear phones, so that others would not be disturbed.

On that first night there were 240 patients in the hospital and no fewer than 56 record requests were played. The very first record, requested by a patient in the maternity ward, was a song by Ben Krass and Curtis Mayfield called 'I want to go to heaven'. In spite of the (perhaps unfortunate) choice of opening song, the first programme went down very well with patients, although when asked for his opinion, 72-year old William Lewis from Causewayhead did admit that 'I don't like this Beatles stuff'.

That year the hospital also lost its tea trolley service, which greatly upset the Friends of Stirling Royal Infirmary who had provided it and who manned it. A reorganisation of facilities now made it redundant, but the loss of the trolley service meant the loss of the £70 income which it generated, and which was used by the Friends to provide other comforts to patients.

In 1964 the hospital was also involved in a huge Civil Defence exercise which took place across central Scotland. This was a time of great Cold War tension between Soviet Russia and the West, when the threat of a missile attack was considerable. This exercise imagined a nuclear attack on Glasgow and an area simulating Pollockshields was set up where Civil Defence members would rehearse their response. For this purpose more than forty Civil Defence personnel established a 'forward medical aid unit' based at Stirling Royal Infirmary. Their job was to screen all casualties to ensure that only the most seriously injured would actually be sent to a 'base hospital', leaving the less serious cases to be treated by first aid and field ambulance people. Looking back from today, it would surely have been an impossible task in the radiation and devastation of a real nuclear war, but at the time Stirling was seen as a vital part of the treatment provision which would have followed such an attack.

Presentation to Matron Jean Ritchie on the occasion of her retrial in 1966.
Miss Ritchie is standing sixth right, and is receiving a gift from Assistant
Matron Miss Marjory Donald. *Courtesy Stirling Council Archives*

In 1966 Matron, Miss Jean Ritchie, announced her decision to retire,
which she did on 31st July that year. Having joined the Infirmary in
1945 she had helped to lead the hospital through an undoubtedly
difficult period in its history. She had coped with the rationing and
austerity of the immediate post-war years, the trauma of transition to
the National Health Service, the problems of a chronic shortage of
nurses and the growth of the hospital to a larger and more challenging
place. In grateful recognition of this service she was presented with a
necklace of pearls, crystal wine glasses and a cheque.

What lay ahead now ? With Stirling University about to open its
doors to students in September 1967, the first priority was a new
maternity wing.

CHAPTER SIX

Miss Plenderleith's Years

1966-1989

In 1966 Miss Florence Mitchell arrived from the Victoria Infirmary in Glasgow to replace Jean Ritchie as Matron at Stirling. In July 1968, however, she left to return to the Victoria Infirmary, now as its Matron. Soon after this move she wrote:

> Although this change was also promotion, it was with great regret that I left Stirling, the hospital, the town, and most of all, the people. Looking back after several months' absence, I know that what I felt to be so strongly alive in Stirling was one of its most valuable assets – the unity between town and hospital, the concern of one for the other, and the uniqueness of this situation. I miss it very much.

In August 1968 Miss Margaret Plenderleith was appointed Matron. Having trained and worked in England, she had moved to Bannockburn Hospital in November 1967, where she happened to be in charge when the great storm of January 1968 occurred. During that stormy night a chimney stack fell through the roof into Ward 3, which necessitated the evacuation of all the patients and staff to Stirling's hospital. This urgent removal included geriatric patients and children (there was even a school at the hospital) and saw Miss Plenderleith striding around the area, torch in hand, guiding ambulances, farmers, firemen and other rescuers through the night past fallen trees and blocked roads to the stricken hospital.

This display of leadership did not go unnoticed and that July Miss Plenderleith was promoted to Matron at Stirling, following the departure of Florence Mitchell. Little did she realise at that time what great changes were about to occur during her time as Matron. One of the first was the question of maternity provision.

In September 1967 the University of Stirling opened its doors for the first time to students. Whether deliberately or unintentionally, the very first student to be admitted was Alastair Gentleman, and so the university's student history began with the enrolment of 'A Gentleman'. In all, a total of 164 undergraduates and 31 post-graduates joined the university in 1967, along with an almost identical number of teaching, technical and administrative staff – a very modest start, but one which would have major repercussions for the Infirmary.

As a result of the opening of the university, the population of the Stirling area was expected to expand rapidly by around 11,000, with implications for a greater demand on the hospital's resources. As a result, a major refurbishment and construction programme began at the infirmary to provide it with the capacity and facilities necessary for this anticipated population growth.

More than three years later the programme of work was still going on. Matron Margaret Plenderleith wrote in the Stirling Nurses' League magazine of February 1971 that,

> Change continues to be the order of the day and at times it is difficult to distinguish the Infirmary from a builder's yard. Bricks and mortar seem to litter every turn you take.

One such development began in July 1967 when it was announced that a new £650,000 maternity unit was to be built at the Infirmary. This was in anticipation of the closure of the County maternity unit at Airthrey Castle; in 1965 the university had bought the Airthrey estate as its campus (now regularly rated as one of the most beautiful in the world) and the Castle would inevitably be required by the university, if not immediately then certainly in future.

Since its opening in the early days of the Second World War, when it received mostly evacuee women, the castle had quickly adapted to its originally-intended post-war role as a County maternity centre. The pre-natal room was on the ground floor to the left of the front door. This was usually the first stop for women brought to Airthrey. The delivery room was on the first floor and featured a large bay window. This room was big enough for two beds and cots – any more than two mothers at a time would have been sent to the maternity unit at Stirling Royal Infirmary. However, since Airthrey Castle served mainly the Bridge of Allan – Hillfoots area the demand for beds was never too great.

Being a castle, not purpose-built as a hospital, the building had its limitations. For example, there was no emergency lighting system.

On one occasion in 1969 a storm caused a power cut, as a result of which one baby was delivered by the night shift ward sister Euphemia (Phemie) Livingstone by tilly lamp light. That such a thing could happen as late as 1969 was surely an indication that a purpose-built facility was now long overdue.

In 2009 the university organised a social history project on Airthrey Castle's time as a maternity home and, following an appeal in the *Stirling Observer*, many people responded with memories of their experiences there, some of which were subsequently published in the university's magazine *Stirling Minds*. These reminiscences give a wonderful picture of life at the Castle during the 1950s and 1960s. For example, the building itself, by its very castle grandeur, made a big impression on both the nurses and the young mothers who were brought there. This ranged from a fascination of the 'dumb waiter' lift shaft, to the 1932 Rolls Royce Shooting Brake that was used as an ambulance, and the deer which grazed (as they still sometimes do) on the lawns outside.

One mother said, 'I liked the tall windows and high ceilings in the castle and remember being taken on a stretcher up a beautiful curved staircase to the delivery room.' Another young mother remembered sneaking out of bed to gaze down onto the staff's New Year Ball, being held in the castle's wood-panelled hall below. To her the scene of Christmas lights and 'dancing couples dressed in their finery' had a magical atmosphere.

One mum, whose baby was born on Christmas Eve, reported that, 'babies born at that time received gifts of matinee jackets, hats and bootees, while the mothers received body lotion and talcum powder. We were allowed to have extra visiting hours and even the food was special.' On Christmas Day there was usually a visit from Santa Claus (although in 1961 he arrived surprisingly early – at 6am!). Later in the day there was always a full Christmas dinner and visitors to the patients were also usually entertained to tea. The staff dance was usually held a few days later, often on December 28th.

Christmas dances at Airthrey Castle were actually often more like parties than proper dances. Although senior staff such as matron, the obstetrics staff (such as Dr Eva Cairns or Dr Elizabeth Rose), management people (often represented by Dr Gordon Harrington), and the castle's own house physician were among the nurses and their guests, the atmosphere was often more like a 'good old fashioned party'

Airthrey Castle's staff at Christmas around 1960. Matron Miss Bunyan is standing fourth from the right. *Photo courtesy Evelyn Duncan*

Halloween party at Airthrey Castle, with the staff dressed up in home-made masks. The only child in the picture is Evelyn Scott, the handyman's daughter. *Photo Evelyn Duncan.*

(as the *Stirling Journal* once described it). The Master of Ceremonies was sometimes one of the staff (as in 1956 when the house physician Dr D G Sandeman took the microphone) but it could also be some local community character (as in 1964 when Jack McLeod's unrivalled wit carried the night along). Interspersed between dances there were usually also entertainers ranging from singers and display dancers to pianists and accordion players. Sometimes there was something different – in 1964 Tommy McCulloch brought along a portable theatre organ, while in 1967 the entertainment included local comedy magician John Shearer. One highlight was always the buffet, usually consisting of delicious home-made fare.

There were, of course, also children's parties at Christmas. One past nurse remembers the party of 1961 which was held in Ward 2. With the beds removed and a decorated Christmas tree stretching to the high ceiling, it was a scene of 'long tables for tea, crackers, Christmas serviettes, children in party clothes and piles of balloons'. Seventy children attended, mostly the families of the patients and their friends. So there were happy times at the Castle.

Christmas may have been an untypical time of year, however. As with any hospital of that time, the regime was very caring, but also undoubtedly strict – one young mother called it 'cold and Victorian' and 'an austere and unwelcoming environment where Matron really did rule supreme'. Nurses who worked there recall a similarly strict atmosphere. Certainly the rules, by today's standards, were authoritarian. No children were allowed to visit, for example. In 1958 premature births were 'discouraged by a diet of cold milk, juice or water with meals and no hot soups or cups of tea', while even after the baby was born, as one woman said, 'my husband and mother were allowed to view our new baby through the nursery window only. Even I wasn't allowed to hold her outside of feeding times – and breast feeding was obligatory, bottle feeding being strictly condemned.' In December 1959 one man brought his wife, already in labour, to the castle door – she was taken in, but then the door was closed in the husband's face as he stood on the front steps.

There were some good times for the staff, however. To begin with the nurses lived in a nearby old farm building called Loch View Cottage but in the early 1950s they moved to a purpose-built extension to the Castle. This wing looks very out of place today, with its rectangular

Loch View Cottage, originally the Airthrey estate's home farm but used as the castle's nursing quarters until the construction of proper staff accommodation in the early 1950s. *Photo courtesy Evelyn Duncan.*

pebble-dashed lines such a contrast to the castle's curving stone grandeur, but at the time it must have been a welcome change from the damp old farm house. The nurses could also play tennis on the

The Packard motor car, used to transport Matron when required, and driven by chauffeur-handyman John Scott (left). *Photo Evelyn Duncan.*

castle's private court and they could fish on Airthrey Loch (where the Health Board ran an angling club). On snowy winter days they sometimes sledged down the grassy slopes around the building.

The castle cook was nurse Mrs Morrill, assisted by Mary McLaughlin who later took over the position. Although they cooked for everyone in the castle, the nurses ate upstairs while the other staff ate downstairs. One of these was John Scott the chauffeur-handyman, whose daughter Evelyn was the only child allowed to run about the castle in those days. She remembers a distinct 'upstairs-downstairs' atmosphere, noticeable even to a little child. 'Dad and I had to use the back entrance and weren't allowed anywhere near the main staircase', she recalls. 'Dad was addressed as 'Scott' – not 'Mr Scott' or 'John'. He was summoned by three rings on the bell in the basement and was on call round the clock. Even Christmas Day wasn't a holiday for him, as the big boilers had to be stoked every few hours'.

During its time as a maternity hospital there seem to have been three matrons. Miss Clark came in 1940, to be followed in the 1950s by Miss Sophie (Sissy) Taylor, and latterly by Miss Kathleen (Kitty) Bunyan. The hospital matron had an office with a fine bay window on the ground floor and a private flat above it with a veranda overlooking Airthrey Loch.

Airthrey Castle continued to serve as the area's maternity hospital even after the university opened in 1967. To begin with the Pathfoot building was the only teaching block on the campus and students from that time can still recall hearing, during their classes, ambulances passing by with bells clanging on their way to the maternity home. Indeed, at least one lecturer is still remembered teaching with an uncharacteristic anxiety to a class of students, who did not discover until later that his wife had been giving birth at the castle while he was teaching them.

Speeches at the opening of the new maternity unit, September 1969.
Photo courtesy Margaret Plenderleith

Lady Younger meets members of the new maternity unit's nursing staff, still wearing white gloves and black stockings just as they did in 1928! *Photo Margaret Plenderleith*

Meanwhile the Infirmary's new replacement maternity unit was under construction at Livilands. The architects were Keppie Henderson and Partners of Glasgow, the same firm which had previously designed the chest infections unit in 1955 (although the actual people who planned it were partners who had joined since then). Begun in August 1967, the scheme was scheduled to take 21 months. The builders were John Laing Construction Ltd, using their 'Laingspan II' system of precast reinforced concrete columns. When completed in 1969 the building provided 81 beds, plus another 20 special baby care beds, to replace the hospital's old maternity unit and the Airthrey Castle facility. The building was opened by Lady Younger of Leckie on 16th September, and was followed by an Open Day when 300-400 members of the public came to admire the new maternity facility.

One noticeable difference from Airthrey Castle was the question of night feeds. At Airthrey Castle, when a new baby cried during the night it was taken into the nursery to be bottle fed so that its mother could have a rest. At the new unit, if a new born baby wanted fed during the night, its mother was woken up to feed it again. As one nurse said, 'this was the new way, but I thought the old way was kinder'. In those days mothers and new-born babies stayed at the maternity unit typically for ten days before being released home.

The completion of the excellent new maternity unit was only one step in a long period of building work at the Infirmary. Better maternity provision required more nurses, so more residences then had to be built – these were opened (at a cost of £195,000) by past matron, Miss Jean Ritchie, who had campaigned long and hard during her time at the Infirmary for this very provision. However, by 1971 Matron Miss Margaret Plenderleith was already saying that,

> . . . in spite of the new residential accommodation opened in October 1969, we are again suffering from a grave shortage of residential accommodation for nursing staff, so in an effort to alleviate this, the Board of Management have rented seven flats in the co-ownership housing scheme at Easter Livilands (one 2-apartment and six 3-apartment flats), and these will be occupied by the Midwifery Superintendent and 12 sisters, thus releasing accommodation within the hospital for junior staff.

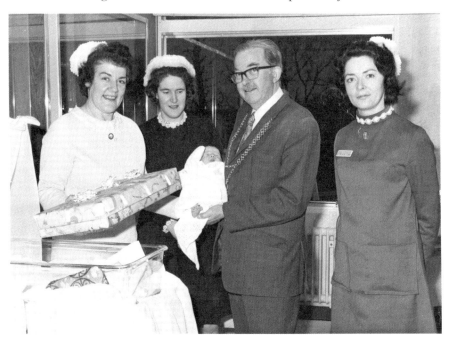

Dr Robert MacIntyre, both a doctor at the hospital and Stirling's provost (1967-1975) admires the first baby to be born at the new maternity unit. Second left, with a slightly anxious look, is Matron Margaret Plenderleith. *Photo courtesy Margaret Plenderleith.*

In December 1970 the foundations were also laid for a new 28-bed medical ward, which eventually opened in early 1972. Meanwhile the old maternity unit was converted into an orthopaedic and accident unit for both males and females, including a 4-bed intensive care unit. As a result of that move, a new female geriatric and medical unit could then be created in Hut 15 where the orthopaedic unit had previously been located.

Looking back on these years, some consultants see it as a wonderful and happy time, in spite of the disruptions of building work. Surgeons were still appointed by a committee in Glasgow, where the Western Regional Hospital Board had its headquarters. The interviewing panel consisted of doctors, consultants, professors and usually just one representative from the Stirling area, '. . . but at least they were medical people' as one doctor said.

Having been appointed, the successful doctor would receive a contract of employment. For some it would mean work at Stirling, but for the urology and vascular surgery specialists it meant eleven clinics or operating sessions per week in a rota round the infirmaries at Stirling, Falkirk and Alloa. In 1969 the Stirling Nurses League magazine joked that a specialist was 'a doctor whose patients are supposed to be ill only during office hours' but in reality this humour was surely unfair – despite any contract, Stirling's urology and vascular doctors worked whatever extra hours were necessary, and would additionally still attend for any emergency brought in to the hospital. 'In those days our work was our life,' said one retired doctor. 'Our commitment to the hospital was pretty total.' When asked if this was different from today, one doctor said, 'The arrangements today . . . the difference is unimaginable . . . '.

Surgeons might train first as younger doctors for nine or ten years before being appointed to a consultancy. Having got there, they understood the importance of working as a team with the junior doctors. Younger doctors were already well trained but the experience of working beside their much more experienced seniors was invaluable.

As with nurses, there was also a great social camaraderie among the hospital's doctors. On at least one occasion, however, a party was sabotaged by nurses. It seems that in the late 1960s Stirling's junior doctors had a habit of neglecting to invite nurses to their parties, so Bill Anderson and his fellow nurses plotted their revenge. Somehow they gained access to one party venue, where they removed the light bulb in the loo and then covered the toilet pan with cellophane. As predicted, young doctors full of drink visited the toilet, discovered that there was no light, and went ahead anyway...

That may have been the junior doctors, but their seniors moved in a different social world. They sometimes golfed, hill-walked, sailed or went to concerts and theatres together. Many invited each other to dinner parties. The Medical Staff Association's functions often also saw retired 'old boys' back to mix with their younger counterparts, where they reminisced and traded stories. These were happy days for Stirling's senior doctors.

Writing in the *Journal of Perioperative Practice* of March 2009, one nurse in England wrote:

> As a novice theatre nurse during the early 1970s, my memories are of a consultant-dominated culture, where senior surgeons influenced what went on with seemingly little or no consideration of anyone else. The hospital was administered by a hospital secretary, whose role was to provide what the surgeons wanted, when they wanted it. Operating sessions were set and adhered to, with a little negotiation in cases of emergency or sometimes personal arrangements.

However this was clearly not the picture at Stirling. The town was too small for such attitudes.

Nurses also look back on the 1960s and 1970s as a very happy time, when lifelong friendships were forged through the teamwork demanded of the job and the fun they had off-duty. One nurse still remembers the discipline even of visiting hours during the 1970s. Before any visitors were allowed in the patients' pillows had to be plumped up, the top cover on the bed had to be straightened perfectly and even the bed wheels were turned inwards so that no-one tripped over them. Meanwhile the patients themselves had their teeth brushed, their hair combed and were made to sit up, leaning back on the plump pillows, 'pretending to look well and happy' as one nurse said with a smile. In those days the maximum number of visitors allowed at the bedside at any one time was only two – visiting cards were issued to visitors, which entitled them entry to the ward while others sat and waited outside.

Socially Stirling's nurses had a great time. Although the nurses' residences were locked at 10pm the girls simply escaped by the windows (and sometimes down drainpipes) and then headed into

Happy nurses, snapped around 1960. *Photo courtesy Mary Ross.*

Stirling to enjoy themselves. When asked about this in 2010, Matron Margaret Plenderleith said 'Of course I knew about it. I was young myself once!' The Terraces Hotel and the Birds and Bees were among the nurses' favourite watering holes, where sometimes the frolics were very un-nurse-like. On one occasion they were thrown out of the Allan Park Hotel when a tasselled bra was seen draped over a chandelier – rumour has it that plaster technician Hugh Clark had something to do with that prank.

Sometimes they received invitations to the army camp at Cultybraggan near Comrie. The soldiers would even send jeeps into Stirling to convey the girls to their camp. On these occasions, however, Sister would stand at the door and prevent the married nurses from going – which, looking back now, they accept was probably for the best.

Bill Anderson was still there, so his pranks also continued. There was the time (he says) when he had himself dressed in a shroud, like a dead body. As the unsuspecting porter pushed his trolley to the mortuary he then slipped his arm out and began caressing the porter's leg, to the poor man's understandable terror. Or the time when he obtained a skeleton and one night fitted it up in the lift, so that it fell out onto the first person who opened the lift door. All part of life at Stirling.

Behind the scenes, however, forces for change were beginning to grow. It is clear that these began with the start of the National Health Service in 1948. During its first twenty years this new, state-run and state funded service seemed to be a model of apparent efficiency. The 1950s and 1960s were a time when new antibiotics and dramatic advances in the treatment of diseases such as tuberculosis appeared, which reduced pressure on hospitals. The improved quality of housing and general affluence of people in post-war Britain also saw a sharp decline in the number of infectious diseases. With fewer demands on beds, hospitals seemed to be successful and more efficient. In fact the need for more expenditure was growing, for during that same time more (and more expensive) advances in medical care began to be made.

By the 1970s changes had started to appear for which the hospitals were not prepared – kidney and liver transplants, heart surgery, joint replacements, the ability to treat malignant diseases like cancer (chemotherapy first began in the 1960s) all began to excite the medical world. These were expensive, however, and it was clear that medium-sized hospitals like Stirling (or Falkirk or Alloa) could not afford to introduce everything they would like to have had. A greater degree of sharing and cooperation became necessary, and the rivalry which undoubtedly existed between Stirling and Falkirk in particular had to be put aside. These were, of course, the first steps in a process which would eventually result in the new Forth Valley Royal Hospital which opened at Larbert in 2010.

In 1970 it was decided to amalgamate the Board of Management for the Stirling and Clackmannan hospitals with that for the Falkirk and District hospitals, and on 1st January 1971 a new Board of Management for Stirling, Falkirk and Alloa Hospitals came into existence. In March 1971 this new board took for its headquarters the Moraig Nurses Home in Stirling, while the old board's offices in Randolph Road were then altered into accommodation for an Audiometric Clinic and a Child Psychiatry centre.

This new board did, of course, inherit the administrative problems which its predecessor, the Western Regional Hospital Board, had faced. A memorandum from November 1973 to the new Board of Management illustrates the pressures which it began to come under. At that time Stirling's two general surgeons spent part of their time either taking clinics or doing operations at the Clackmannan County Hospital in Alloa. Not surprisingly, this arrangement 'resulted in mutual lack of understanding between the two infirmaries of the other's surgical requirements', which was clearly unsatisfactory and inefficient. Stirling's urological specialists were in an even more awkward situation. Not only did they perform general surgery at both Stirling and Alloa but, additionally, undertook all urological surgery in Stirling, Alloa and Falkirk, including emergencies. This was also plainly unsuitable, as their memorandum argued:

> To maintain a urological service, two consultant surgeons have to receive emergencies in 3 widely separated hospitals and be responsible for inpatient care in these 3 hospitals – a wholly unacceptable situation.

> The existing arrangement requires the duplication of expensive specialist instrumentation in 3 hospitals.

These were trying times for the Board of Management.

The administration of hospitals was also drastically changed at this time by the Salmon Report. This was first produced in 1965 and gradually implemented thereafter, so that the 'Salmon Scheme' actually came into force in the Stirling area in 1971. Salmon set up a new hospital nursing structure which included the ending of the post of Matron, to be replaced by a Chief Nursing Officer, with subsidiary Senior Nursing Officers. And so Miss Margaret Plenderleith became the Stirling Royal Infirmary's last Matron and its first Chief Nursing Officer. She could see this coming when she wrote in the Stirling Nurse' League magazine of 1971:

> The Salmon Structure for the Stirling, Falkirk and Alloa Hospitals was sent to the Scottish Home and Health Department on 1st February 1971, and we now await its return for further discussion on its implementation. It may be that when I next write to you I shall be nameless: just a number.

The Chief Nursing Officer was a much more administrative job. On the one hand it disappointed many nurses because it pointed their career pathway towards administration, when so many wanted to work as medical carers. On the other hand it encouraged career people, especially more men, to join the nursing profession – a change which eventually even forced the Royal College of Nursing to admit male members to the organisation (indeed, James Macmillan had already become an Assistant Matron at the Infirmary in 1970). This change is well summed up by Ian Scott is his history of Falkirk Royal Infirmary, *Touch Ane Touch A'*:

> It was to be goodbye Matron . . . and welcome Principal or Senior Nursing Officer! Days of sex equality and increasing numbers of male nurses in the service brought doubts about titles like 'Matron' and 'Sister' and the neutral names were the result. The changes were not welcomed by many and it was clear that staff, patients and the general public preferred the friendly and the familiar, but while few endorsed the new approach, it was imposed.

Before long, reaction to this change began to be voiced. In the Stirling Nurses' League magazine of 1975, the editor spoke for many in an article on sex equality which said:

> . . . In how many other ways will the anti-discrimination act affect the ladies ? In the nursing profession – not many. It would appear that the men have all got well up the ladder and have already snaffled the top posts. They may hold the top jobs but they do not hold the most important jobs or the most satisfying ones.

And so the 'Salmon wind of change . . . ' (as one disgruntled letter to the *British Medical Journal* called it) blew through the Infirmary, bringing still more upheaval.

On the other hand, there is no doubt that the institution did need some kinds of change. By the 1970s the Infirmary was operating with huge budgets and running a staff of hundreds, which required a much higher degree of professional management, business and administrative skill than ever before, far beyond the abilities of the local lawyers who once acted as treasurers and secretaries to the hospital in its early days. By 1973 the Infirmary employed 60 doctors, 141 registered nurses, 21 enrolled nurses, 127 student nurses, 53 pupil nurses, 89 'other' nurses, 42 medical auxiliaries, 54 administrative and clerical staff, 259 domestic and ancillary staff, 3 tradesmen, 19 laundry staff and 24 other types of staff – a total of 892 employees. If only the town councillors who first began to consider a hospital for Stirling in 1871 could have imagined where their ideas would lead one hundred years later!

In spite of all these changes, life at the hospital did, of course, go on as usual. Patients needed care, and nurses and doctors continued

Farewell to Assistant Matron, Miss Marjory Donald, in 1970. Seated on her right
is Matron Margaret Plenderleith. *Photo courtesy Margaret Plenderleith.*

to work on, no matter who their political or managerial masters were.
On the medical front, doctors gradually began to specialise more. One
surgeon called it, 'a move from special interest to full-blown speciality'.
This began in 1973 when urology became a separate speciality distinct
from the general surgery still performed by Stirling's surgeons at that
time. Soon vascular surgery followed, and so patients ranging from
those requiring artery bypasses to those suffering ruptured aortic
aneurisms were now treated by a specialist at Stirling. Those with a
wide range of other problems such as gastric ulcers, appendicitis,
varicose veins and so on continued to be treated by the general
surgeons.

Throughout this time Stirling's public continued to support the
town's hospital. In 1966 the Stirling Women's Voluntary Service
donated a piano to the Infirmary; it had rubber wheels so that it could
be taken quietly into any ward. In 1967 the Dunblane Round Table
organisation donated £1,350 towards a cardiac machine – one of the
exciting new pieces of equipment of that time. In 1968 a new waiting
room opened; this included a tea stall manned by local WRVS ladies
and a children's playroom staffed at weekends by Girl Guides and Red

Cross attendants. In 1970 the Society of Friends of Stirling Royal Infirmary furnished a day room at the hospital, provided 'pillow telephones' for patients, TV sets for the nurses' home and donated (and regularly rotated) books to the hospital's library. All signs of a remarkable level of public support which could be traced back for a century in Stirling.

Unfortunately no amount of support could help with the hospital's staffing problems. As the decade of the 1970s dawned, there continued to be a serious shortage of nurses across Britain, including at Stirling. At the 1970 prize-giving ceremony Miss Scott-Wright, Director of Nursing Studies at Edinburgh University, wanted married nurses to return to the profession. By all means stay at home while the children were growing up, she said, but then return to the Infirmary and resume an interesting and rewarding career. 'Married women must in future be willing to come back, and to learn more', she said. 'As more complicated equipment is developed, nurses have to step up their technical ability. Patients rely on them for assurance.'

During this time many long-serving members of staff, one by one, retired. In 1968 Sister Ena Elvin retired after 22 years' service. One nurse later wrote, 'I shall never forget the awe and respect in which I held Sister Elvin....I can safely say that the instruction and inspiration given to me during my first three months in Ward 4 securely built the foundation of my whole period of training in SRI'.

Another was Assistant Matron, Miss Marjory Donald, who retired in 1970. As she looked back on her time at the Infirmary there was one change which she certainly did not miss:

> Missing from the wards today – and with no regret on my part – is that abomination 'The Aspidistra'. There were literally dozens in every ward and they seemed to hold a special place in Sister's affections. They had to be soaked and bathed weekly, and all leaves sponged. Some were the size of small trees and when soaked almost required a weightlifter to convey them back to their personal window ledge. I must have presented a comical sight carrying these enormous pots with leaves completely obscuring me from waist up. All that was visible to the human eye was an aspidistra with short legs and feet (same clad in sensible walking shoes and good black cashmere stockings) proceeding down the ward. It must have been an unnerving sight for someone recovering from an anaesthetic.

One change which many did regret was the disappearance of the old nurses' uniform. To nurses of the time, their uniform was a source

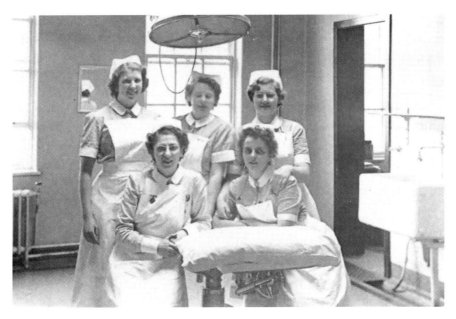

Nurses, proud of their smart uniform at work . . . .

. . . and off duty.   *Photos Stirling Council Archives (top) and Mary Ross (bottom).*

of immense pride and a badge of their skills. They took pride in being always immaculate – many nurses possessed three uniforms and about ten aprons so that they could be changed and laundered every day. Aprons were especially liable to get stained or dirtied in the routine of daily work. Now, suddenly, the proudly starched cuffs and apron were gone, and the iconic starched frilly hat was replaced by a paper cap, to the huge dismay of nurses. All kinds of comments appeared in the Stirling Nurses' League magazine, such as the retired nurse in 1971 who was:

> . . . sad to hear the apron has disappeared. I wonder what nurses do now when a clumsy new house doctor, trying to get a blood transfusion going, lets blood spurt all over her clean frock.

Or the nurse who wrote:

> I feel very strongly about the cap; if the cap goes, a lot of dignity and confidence will go too. I am young enough to be with it in many ways, but old enough to want the dignity of a profession retained, and I feel the cap is a 'must'.

This discontent rumbled on for years at Stirling. As late as 1978 the magazine's editor wrote:

> Gone is the attractive cap of the Student Nurse which did much to endear her to patients, visitors and medical students alike; long before her proficiency in nursing skills impressed anyone. Gone too the gleaming white apron and the different coloured uniforms and in many cases gone the uniform. Why, oh why? Now all look alike. It is democracy gone mad....
>   It wouldn't really matter all that much if all we'd lost had been a few starched collars and cuffs, but much else has gone with them. Where is the dignity, the pride in appearance, the self respect and the respect for others be they junior or senior or merely a patient? Is 'merely' the operative word here? Surely not! Let it never be said that it is so in Stirling Royal Infirmary.'

Looking back now, the question of uniforms was a relatively small matter which nevertheless stirred up very strong feelings among nurses. Someone, somewhere, was able to say with pride, or perhaps sadness, 'I was the last nurse at Stirling to wear a frilly cap'. However, outside the hospital much bigger events and upheavals were about to happen.

As the decade of the 1970s began to unfold, great industrial unrest spread through Britain. Early signs were the miners' strike of 1972 and the workers' campaign to save the Upper Clyde shipyards. Then in 1973 Britain joined the European Common Market (now the EU) and the Yom Kippur war between Israel and its Arab neighbours saw the price of oil rise in Britain by 400%. By November inflation in Britain was up at 18%. The miners went on an overtime ban, and Edward Heath's Conservative government imposed a pay freeze which quickly resulted in strikes by workers ranging from civil servants and gas workers to London dockers and Glasgow firemen. There were shortages of everything from sugar and toilet rolls to petrol and bread.

Of course these events impacted on the Infirmary. From as early as 1968 health workers had been on the march, as described in a remarkable editorial in the Stirling Nurses League magazine of 1969:

> During 1968, readers will agree that we have enjoyed or suffered – according to our views – a surfeit of Demonstrations, Protest Marches, "Sit-ins" and Lock-outs, mostly by students but also by others . . . Even the Nursing Profession managed to invade the House of Commons – to what effect we still don't know.
>
> The students certainly have been given the limelight, and whether all their complaints are fully justified is a debatable point, but there is never smoke without fire. The only section of the community calling themselves students who have not protested in public are the nursing students. Are their conditions so ideal that no protest is necessary? Doubtful! The reason for the calm is more likely to be the apathy with which they approach their nursing career, their lack of leadership and their inability to speak with one voice or indeed to speak at all.
>
> The Editor does not advocate student revolts in Hospitals. Conditions could be improved without that . . . The people in hospital who could justifiably protest and proclaim their rights are the patients.
>
> The right to remain a person, not a number or a case.
>
> The right to decide whether or not they will act the part of a guinea pig and, if so, for the benefit of whom ?
>
> The right to appointments kept in Clinics and Out-patient Departments.
>
> The right to see the same nurse two nights running instead of a different one each night.
>
> The right to sleep when they want and not to order.
>
> The right to eat a meal undisturbed by chief's visits or X-ray appointments   (. . . . and so on, in similar vein!)

In February 1971, following an outcry in the national press about the 'great unwashed' – patients who were unwashed because of the shortage of nurses – the editor of the *Nursing Times* was interviewed on radio, when she presented a picture of diminishing numbers of nurses and the rest struggling to cope with an impossible workload. The Stirling Nurses League magazine reflected that same feeling in its 1971 edition when the editor wrote:

> For far too long this nation has accepted the unfailing service of the nursing profession as something that was built in with life itself, and therefore working conditions and salaries were not their responsibility. Only when the well runs dry is the water missed – and the helpless dirty.

Clearly there was great discontent among the nurses. The first big health strike occurred in 1972 when 97,000 NHS employees across Britain took industrial action. Nurses' anger again boiled over in 1974, leading to them marching to Downing Street, demonstrating outside parliament and holding a rally in London's Hyde Park. An independent inquiry into nurses' pay led by Lord Halsbury followed; the report which resulted in 1974 led to a pay rise for health workers of an average 30%.

With the miners' action causing coal shortages to power stations, the government began a 'three-day week' strategy on 1st January 1974 (which did not end until 7th March). Electricity supplies were limited to just three days a week to most commercial operations in an effort to conserve fuel stocks. Even TV broadcasting had to stop at 10.30 pm. Not surprisingly, power supplies were prioritised to hospitals. No operations or other serious treatments were disrupted by power cuts, and in 1974 Matron Margaret Plenderleith was able to report, with masterly dry comment, that 'We are not badly affected by reduced power but the Recreation Hall is without heating'.

In fact there *were* problems. Health, catering and laundry workers, mostly from Glasgow, regularly picketed the hospital gates. Senior staff often did the hospital's laundry. Even Miss Plenderleith helped – 'I've never peeled so many potatoes!' she said later, having helped out at Falkirk for a day. Bus working hours changed because of shop stewards' objections and this forced nurses' shift hours to be changed. Nurses going to work at the Orchard House hospital also had to go through the unnerving experience of entering past pickets waiting there.

Meanwhile the economic difficulties of that time resulted in a freeze on new building programmes which delayed the start of several schemes at Stirling. With inflation remaining high, people demanded high pay settlements, whether from the Conservative government or the Labour one which followed in 1974. During the 1970s the number of strikes averaged between 2000 and 3000 a year, every year.

However, in the middle of this time of great turmoil, another upheaval occurred when the ancient county of Stirlingshire was abolished in 1973, to be replaced by a combination with Clackmannanshire, unimaginatively known as Central Region. This area was then sub-divided into the 'Districts' of Stirling, Falkirk and Clackmannan, within which more local matters could be administered. Health care, however was not one of them and remained a regional matter.

On 31st March 1974 the Board of Management for Stirling, Falkirk and Alloa Hospitals (which had only come into existence in 1971) was therefore also abolished, to be replaced by the Forth Valley Health Board; it had responsibility, not only for the hospitals in its area, but also for all health care in the Region. In a very appropriate move, this new body decided to use the old Stirling Royal Infirmary building in Spittal Street (which had been standing mostly empty since 1928) as

The old infirmary building in Spittal Street finds a new role as headquarters of the Forth Valley Health board in 1974. *Photo courtesy Stirling Council Archives*

its new Headquarters. For some of the staff it was a strange experience, moving into the old wards with their memories and even some surviving signs of the old days. One worker still remembers turning an old sluice room into a filing cupboard and thinking back to the nurses who must have used that same place when the building was a hospital.

In June that same year Stirling Royal Infirmary reached its hundredth year of existence. With the paint hardly dry on the walls, this centenary event was marked by a reception in that same old building in Spittal Street where the Infirmary had first opened. This function was attended by members of the new health board, members of past Boards of Management, members of the Town Council, the Infirmary's last medical superintendent Dr Gordon Harrington and Stirling's provost and hospital consultant Dr Robert McIntyre, plus past and present members of the hospital staff. It was a gathering, the likes of which had not been seen since the opening of the 'new' hospital in 1928.

An anniversary cake was ceremonially cut by 19 year old student-nurse Isobel Philp of Torryburn and, at the suggestion of the board Chairman James Macreadie, the cake was then presented to the infirmary's geriatric patients, so that young and old were tied together by the history of the same place. Among the speeches, Dr McIntyre toasted the future of the town's hospital and said that he hoped that all the best of human values for which the infirmary had stood in the past would be maintained in the future.

The hospital's centenary celebration was an event which was well reported in the local press, but during these years there were other stories which have also stuck in local people's memories.

During the 1970s there were several local 'bomb scares', for example. The '70s was a time of troubles in Ireland, when at least fourteen terrorist bombs exploded in England, mostly in London, during those ten years. Targets included several pubs, but also Oxford Street, Harrods, the House of Commons and the Earls Court exhibition centre. Six people were killed and over 360 injured by these bombs.

This led to a spate of bomb scares, as people all over Britain reported unattended suspicious looking bags or packages to the police. More than once the Thistles shopping centre in Stirling had to be evacuated as a precaution until the offending packages could be checked, but the hospital also experienced at least four bomb scares during those years.

Black ties and beautiful long dresses – it must be another 1970s staff function at the
Golden Lion hotel. *Photo courtesy Margaret Plenderleith.*

Then there was the time when a group of boys got caught out on
the Campsie Fells when the weather turned bitterly cold. Three lads
died of hypothermia but the survivors were brought to Stirling for
treatment at the Infirmary. While they waited in Casualty one boy is
reported to have asked for a cup of tea, but this was declined. Next day
the papers were full of stories claiming 'Heroes on the mountainside
refused a cup of tea', which greatly upset the staff. The truth was that
they were refused a cup of tea because a proper hot meal was already
waiting for them to eat, complete with hot drinks.

On a brighter note, there was the story of the hospital's lion cub.
The Muir family of Blair Drummond had a long history of supporting
the hospital, so when the Blair Drummond Safari Park opened in 1970
the hospital's matron Miss Plenderleith was invited to the event. It
seems that she joked to Sir John Muir that she would love to have a
lion and so, much to her surprise, a lion cub called Doune was duly
brought to the hospital soon after. Apart from chewing at Matron's
finger the cub was an instant hit in the Children's Ward, where the
young patients were allowed to feed it with a bottle. At the end of the

day Doune was then taken to Matron's flat, where it stayed until collected by people from Chipperfield's Circus who put it into their 'pets corner'.

On another occasion a painting by the celebrity entertainer and artist Rolf Harris was somehow acquired by Bill Anderson, who was at that time a charge nurse in the children's ward (where the painting was then hung). Bill eventually went on through the medical and geriatric units to become a Nursing Officer – but clearly his potential was spotted back in those days on the children's ward (in spite of his previous history of some dreadful practical jokes).

During the 1970s the hospital's annual dinner dance continued to provide the press with photo-shots of people in evening dress. By now these evenings were invariably held at the Golden Lion hotel and were normally attended 'by all ranks' as one nurse put it. However it was also important that senior staff 'knew not to cross the familiarity line', as Miss Plenderleith recalled in 2010. Or as one nurse said, 'They might chat to us, but we knew never to speak first to someone who was senior to us. And we *never* called anyone senior by their first name...'.

Christmas also remained a highlight in the hospital year, a time when traditions established a hundred years earlier were maintained. Many wards had their own Christmas tree and were brightened with decorations often donated by local shops. Children always had stockings for Christmas morning, filled with gifts donated by local shops and wrapped by hospital staff. On Christmas day the staff would 'ruin everyone's day by going round the wards singing carols – at 6.30 in the morning!' as one nurse said. The singers consisted of 'whichever staff had got up in time, mostly Sisters, Nursing Officers and staff coming on duty – but I don't think Matron *ever* had a Christmas Day off'.

During these years the hospital also began to form new links with the local community. Representatives attended the careers conventions increasingly being held at local schools. The Infirmary also held its own 'Careers in Hospital' exhibitions for local pupils. These were staged, usually for three days, in the nurses' Recreation Hall and always featured a wide variety of occupations ranging from careers in physiotherapy, radiography, laboratory or pharmacy work to occupational therapy and even catering.

In 1970 the police also held 'teach-ins' at local high schools including Stirling High, St Modans and Alloa Academy. This was a community initiative first begun by Sergeant Robert Johnston of the (then) Stirling and Clackmannan Police Force. On these occasions Miss Plenderleith joined other local dignitaries such as senior policemen, church leaders, council officers and the school headmaster on a panel to discuss with pupils issues ranging from comprehensive education, vandalism, corporal and capital punishment, or abortion, sex and marriage, to crime and violence, teacher shortages and contraception.

During the 1970s the hospital especially formed closer links with the Queen Victoria School at Dunblane for the children (originally only boys) of people in the armed services – indeed, a picture used to hang in the hospital staff dining room of the first boy to 'pass out' from this school. During the 1970s boys from the school would often undertake some community service by helping for a few days at the hospital. Here they would help the porters, push trolleys and do other useful tasks.

By the later 1970s the strikes and upheavals of the early part of the decade seemed to be over and the delayed building programme resumed. In spite of the similarly-disruptive 'winter of discontent' of 1978-1979 (which heralded the fall of the Labour government and the start of the 'Thatcher years'), building work somehow managed to continue. Nurses' teaching was moved to the Callendar Park College at Falkirk, which allowed the hospital's teaching unit to be turned into a new ward (ward 10). A new £150,000 Eye Clinic was also built, adjoining ward 12. On 10th August 1978 this Ophthalmic Unit was officially opened by local MP Harry Ewing, who was also Parliamentary Under-Secretary of State at the Scottish Office. On this day he also planted a maple tree outside the Intensive Care Unit but, in spite of its location close to intensive care, the tree died, or as Miss Plenderleith recorded afterwards, 'it was unsuccessfully resuscitated and only commemorated the occasion for a few weeks'. Work also began on an additional Day Bed Unit which was opened in December 1978 and received its first patients on 8th January 1979. So the 'builder's yard' continued to be busy.

Although the new blocks were eagerly anticipated there is no doubt that, while the work progressed, the staff and patients required great tolerance. As Miss Plenderleith wrote in 1979:

In the past few months we have lived with the noise of excavators and the vibration of drillers. However I am sure all the dirt and inconvenience will be worthwhile when we have our new Theatres, Surgical Block, etc.

By mid-1979 work had begun to pass a power cable to the site of the new surgical block and a 'huge ravine' lay at the side of ward 11 and the X-ray department. Staff trying to reach ward 10 had to wear Wellington boots and 'keep close to the Laundry'.

This building work went on for many more years. It was undoubtedly a difficult time for the hospital's management and in 1982 Miss Margaret Plenderleith took early retirement, having served as Matron for fourteen years. At a retirement dinner held at Bellsdyke Hospital she was presented with a cheque and a crystal paperweight in recognition of her service to the hospital during such difficult years. In a nice touch, she was allowed to retire with the title Matron, rather than the new label of Chief Nursing Officer.

Miss Plenderleith then moved to work for the Nurses Benevolent Fund, a cause which she had long supported and where she later became its Secretary (and for which she received an MBE in 1997).

During the 1980s little changes began to appear in the life of the hospital. For example, although there was now a self-service canteen for staff, senior doctors and nursing staff generally used the waitress-service section where there was a more – 'up-market' atmosphere. By the later 1980s this had gone and everyone had to use the self-service cafe. Junior doctors still had a small private lounge and senior staff still had their common room, usually known as the 'green room' because of its green chairs, but the atmosphere was changing.

The Medical Staff Association annual dinner-dance still continued, but that was generally for consultants and their wives and was a black-tie affair. On the other hand, the annual hospital dance at the Golden Lion hotel began to decline, and although a 'hospital night' was later introduced it was generally attended by the infirmary's doctors, anaesthetists and radiographers. 'By then, even junior doctors were paid much more than nurses of even ten years experience', said one doctor later. 'So I don't remember nurses at those evenings'.

By the 1980s the work-load of a typical consultant general surgeon (there were three at Stirling) was two half-day clinics and three half-day theatre lists per week. In addition, however, they shared the evening and weekend work, so each would be on call every third day and every third night, and every third weekend. How often they were called at night could depend on the personality of the individual. Having left their junior doctors to do a list of 'straightforward' operations, some consultants would still want to be called if any complications occurred, such as a particularly inflamed appendix.

Meanwhile building work still went on at the hospital. In the spring of 1985 work began on what was laughingly called (had it not been so ironic) 'Phase 1 of the re-development of Stirling Royal Infirmary'. This would eventually turn into the Queen Elizabeth Wing but its creation seemed to take an eternity. The project included negotiations with the Livilands Bowling Club which eventually saw it move to a new site in Randolph Road while the club's previous grounds (including a croquet lawn) disappeared under a car park.

The main architect of the Queen Elizabeth Wing was Mr J Millar of the NHS's CSA Building Division of Glasgow, supported by Davie and McCulloch mechanical and electrical engineers of Glasgow, Woolgar, Hunter and Partners civil and structural engineers of Glasgow, and Wilkinson and Lowe quantity surveyors of Glasgow. The main contractor was Balfour Beatty Construction (Scotland) Ltd,

This 1960s aerial view of the hospital shows the Livilands Bowling Club and clubhouse top left, screened from the hospital by trees and shrubs. This area became the car park in front of the new Queen Elizabeth wing.

with Hayden Young Ltd of Glasgow as sub-contracted mechanical engineers and Drake and Scull (Scotland) Ltd of Dundee as sub-contracted electrical engineers.

When completed in late 1988 the impressive new wing contained 216 surgical beds served by five operating theatre suites, a minor surgery and endoscopy theatre, a radiodiagnostic department complete with the latest CAT scanners, ultrasound and angiography equipment, an intensive therapy unit, a coronary care unit, a pharmacy (complete with its own sterile production unit), a laboratory block with various 'satellite' departments ranging from microbiology to nuclear medicine, a computerised admissions unit and support facilities ranging from linen storage to staff changing rooms.

According to the colourful booklet produced by the hospital to mark the opening of the new wing, the

> . . . advanced theatre suite uses a table top transfer system which means that the patient brought in on a special trolley or bed is moved virtually automatically into position for their operation. This means the minimum of movement for the patient.

> In one of the theatres a sophisticated system provides ultra clean air for special types of surgery such as hip replacement where the risk of infection must be reduced to the absolute minimum.

> A special feature of the theatre-suite is its post-operative recovery area where patients who have been operated on recover under the specialist care of the anaesthetist and trained theatre staff before returning to the ward.

> Patients will find the wards offer a new level of comfort and convenience. There are single, four or six bed rooms each with its own washing and toilet facilities and the decoration and furnishings match the best hotel standards.

The total cost was approximately £18 million, of which £4 million was for the high quality equipment installed. The additional cost of running this new wing was estimated in 1988 to be £800,000 per annum.

Finally, on 29th September 1989 the new wing was officially opened by Her Majesty Queen Elizabeth the Queen Mother who, as the Duchess of York, had previously opened the new infirmary with her husband in 1928. The ceremonial party included Colonel James Stirling, Lord Lieutenant of Stirlingshire, Mrs Iris Isbister, Chair of

Accompanied by Mrs Iris Isbister, Chair of the Forth Valley Health Board, the Queen Mother waves to the crowds of onlookers. *Photo Stirling Council Archives*

The Queen Mother is escorted by Colonel Stirling, Lord Lieutenant of Stirlingshire. Local MP Michael Forsyth on the right. *Stirling Council Archives*

The Queen Mother meets hospital chaplain the Rev J Lamb. *Photo Stirling Council Archives*

the Forth Valley Health Board, Mr Michael Forsyth the local MP and Minister of Health in Scotland, and the Rev J Lamb the Hospital Chaplain.

Having unveiled a plaque to name the new building, Her Majesty made a tour of the facility before enjoying afternoon tea and then viewing photographs of her previous visit in 1928. However the over-riding impression from photographs taken on the day is of her natural warmth and charm, as she chatted with patients and nurses during her visit. It was a very happy and successful occasion.

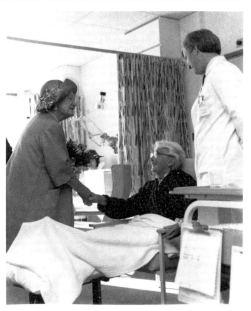

What photographs do *not* reveal, however, is that the pretty flowers seen by the Queen Mother as she approached the building to open it had actually been specially painted in her favourite colours. The day before, Chief Executive Officer Miss Barry got Bill Anderson to spray paint the pastel coloured carnations a brighter pink and blue so that it would please Her Majesty.

The Queen Mother meets staff and patients as she tours the wards of the new wing. *Photo courtesy Stirling Council Archives*

'We were used to repainting things for visiting VIPs,' said Bill later, with a smile. 'In those days local MP Michael Forsyth, who was also Scotland's Minister for Health, seemed to be around the hospital quite a lot. Every time he visited we had, for some reason, to repaint all the trolleys – when we smelled new paint we knew that Mr Forsyth was on his way. So painting the flowers for the Queen Mother was nothing special! They even had me out for a rehearsal the night before, pacing the route which the Queen Mother would walk, in order to know how many seconds it would take'. At least that's how Bill remembers the day.

As onlookers waved and smiled at the royal visitor, and snapped their photos in the sunshine, little did any of them realise what further changes lay ahead. Who would have known that the hospital building

With great natural warmth the Queen Mother chats with onlookers and disabled patients outside the new wing. *Photo courtesy Stirling Council Archives*

which the Duchess of York had opened in 1928, and to which she had now returned as Queen Mother in 1989 to open a gleaming, state of the art, multi-million pound extension, was already being pencilled in to merge with the hospital at Falkirk, to lose many of its departments and facilities, and eventually to lose even its royal name.

CHAPTER SEVEN

The Forth Valley Years

1989-2011

The opening of the Queen Elizabeth wing at Stirling Royal Infirmary was not the solution to problems which the hospital faced. Even as it opened, some doctors regretted the money spent on its construction – some already believed that only a completely new, centralised, hospital would answer the long-term needs of central Scotland. Although people might not have realised it at the time, the opening of the new wing marked the beginning of a period of almost constant transition, as the hospital's administrators and management struggled to balance costly advances in medical care with changing social expectations and demands. Unfortunately for them, there was now also a new factor to juggle with – politics.

By 1989 Margaret Thatcher had been prime minister of a Conservative government for already ten years. During this time there is no doubt that Britain's health services were politicised more than ever before. As 'waiting lists' hit the headlines many hospitals found themselves under pressure to respond and there were reports that, in some cases, resources were moved from one area of care to another. Such concerns were an unwelcome distraction when policy makers faced long term planning decisions on such things as the care of a growing elderly population, cancer treatment, or Scotland's chronic problem of heart disease.

Gradually the hospital secretaries, matrons and medical superintendents (the 'triumvirate' as one retired consultant later called them) who had run hospitals for a hundred years, but who were almost invariably from a medically-trained background rather than a management-trained one, began to disappear. In their place came the 'Chief Executive' and a new breed of professional managers. They had very different, more business-like, attitudes to hospital costs, staffing, bed management and so on and almost inevitably relations between doctors and management became strained under the growing administrative pressure for change.

One example was a proposal, put forward by the Conservative government in a White Paper of 1989, that hospitals might 'opt out' of National Health Service administration and become self-governing Trusts which would then bid for NHS work. This was a policy strongly supported by Scotland's Home Secretary Michael Forsyth (and who was also Stirling's Conservative MP), but just as strongly opposed (in 1989) by 37 Forth Valley consultants and, according to the *Stirling Observer*, no fewer than 94.5% of the Forth Valley Health Board workforce (who believed that Trusts would cut wages and working conditions in order to make their bids cheap enough to win contracts).

Another trend was the appearance of several new private hospitals across Scotland. One was the £3 million Kings Park Hospital which opened at Stirling in 1990. It included an acute surgical unit of twenty beds, with an operating theatre, physiotherapy and X-ray facilities. Although there had always been some private beds at Stirling Royal Infirmary, the last lingering signs of the pre-NHS years, these had already dwindled to a very few and with the opening of the Kings Park Hospital the last of these disappeared. Indeed, for a time, the Infirmary's more business-driven management was even able to use some of the private hospital's underused capacity to help reduce their own waiting lists and so ease pressure at the Infirmary. Nevertheless, the very fact that the Infirmary had to send patients to the local private hospital, and pay to use the facilities there, was one indicator of the growing pressures which now existed at Stirling, even with its new wing.

As the 1990s progressed, so did talk of Trusts. In January 1991 the *Stirling Observer* reported that Forth Valley Health Board had 'denied a claim that it has secret plans to push for trust status at the hospital'. Nevertheless, although 'Consultants opposed the idea of NHS trust status for Stirling last year, it is understood that the matter is to be discussed again by the medical staff association at the hospital', the paper added. So the idea was gaining ground, at least among doctors.

In April 1992 the Conservatives, now led by Prime Minister John Major, won another general election. Then in May 1992 the Scottish Office awarded the Infirmary £500,000 to improve its day surgery provision. This money would enable a thousand more patients to be treated in the first year, which would free up in-patient beds for more appropriate use. Nevertheless, the hidden hand of government was immediately suspected by some to be behind this move. 'SRI cash boost renews trust fears', said the *Stirling Observer*, expressing union fears that 'the additional facilities would make Stirling Royal an even more attractive proposition for opting-out'.

On May 20th 1992 the *Stirling Observer* carried a strong denial by the Forth Valley Health Board that it would 'formally apply for trust status within weeks'. On 24th June, however, the paper's headline read 'SRI to go it alone' above a report which confirmed that the Forth Valley Health Board had, indeed, made a last-minute expression of interest in Trust Status.

These were early days in the story of trusts, and the consequences of granting trust status were not yet clear or certain. Indeed, during a parliamentary debate on May 1st 1991, Scottish Labour MP Sam Galbraith said:

> The debate today, which is about the consultation that must take place before a hospital opts out, comes at an especially significant time. Guy's hospital, the flagship of opting out in England, is already in severe financial difficulties and must shed jobs. The cuts in services at Guy's hospital are being made not because the services are not needed but because, in the words of the chief executive, they are "not profitable". I repeat, it is not because the services are not needed, but because they are not profitable. . . . . The Government will only be able to approve applications against widespread opposition; and they will have to, in Bill Fyfe's own words, "force them down the throats" of the people of Scotland.

Given this kind of argument in parliament, local unions were furious at the Forth Valley Health Board's announcement. National Union of Public Employees local spokesman John Lyons said 'We have to question whether the standard of patient care will remain as high under trust status. There is evidence from self governing hospitals down south that staff wages and conditions are downgraded and profit is put before patient care'. This was a view also shared by Margaret Davidson of the recently formed Stirling and District Patients' Association, who said she was 'very worried about the standard of patient care under trust status'. Labour district councillor Jack McConnell, sensing the public mood, declared, 'People will live to regret the impact of opting out and we will oppose any attempts to give Stirling Royal trust status. The Government has to be made aware of the community's opposition to the proposal'.

Of course the Conservative view was quite different. 'NHS trust status will be a means of improving still further the hospital's contribution to the National Health Service,' argued local Conservative MP Michael Forsyth. 'In expressing an interest it joins a growing band of hospitals which will remain part of the NHS but which believe they can offer better patient care if they have more freedom to manage their own affairs. The record of existing Trusts is one of reduced waiting lists and substantial increases in the number of patients treated', he added.

The hospital management's 'expression of interest' was duly followed by the awarding of full Trust Status in April 1993, followed later by a similar opt-out by Falkirk and District Royal Infirmary. Although now able to manage themselves, both hospitals still remained answerable to the Forth Valley Health Board, which also continued to manage 'primary care' such as local health centres in the community.

The Stirling Royal Infirmary NHS Trust was initially led by Chief Executive Keith Thomson, who had previously been the hospital's General Manager. In early 1994 he left to take a position at a group of hospitals in north Wales, and he was replaced in May by Plean-born Alan Hunter. He was welcomed by local surgeon George McKelvie, now Chairman of the Stirling Royal Infirmary NHS Trust who said 'I am sure Alan will provide the leadership we need to take our hospital successfully through the next exciting stages of its development'.

In fact the change to trust status did *not* result in the lowering of standards feared by some. As the *Stirling Observer* reported in September 1993:

> In the five short months since hoisting the flag of NHS Trust status above Stirling Royal Infirmary, both captain and crew appear highly contented with the course so far charted.
>
> Mutinous dissent forecast during the consultation process has failed to materialise and, if the optimism apparent at least week's open meeting of the Trust board of directors is a mirror of general staff and patient satisfaction, then all is very well indeed....
>
> Certainly, secrecy is not in the manifesto for the board of directors. Requirements state that they need hold only one open meeting annually. At Stirling three such meetings occur and a bulletin of the content of these is quickly distributed to staff.

Change, however, continued to be constant. Hospital management continued to press for shorter waiting lists. Young house doctors were

Receptionist Lisa Tyler

increasingly expected to work longer hours. Patients found themselves going home after treatment much sooner than ever before, often to the great frustration of the doctors. Surgeons had to learn new skills such as keyhole surgery and the use of fibre optics. Nurses found themselves having to cope with an increasing array of complicated and extremely expensive equipment, ranging from CAT scan machines (priced at around £250,000 in 1994) to Ultrasound equipment (which was also very costly, at about £110,000 per machine at that time). Not surprisingly stress spread through the workforce. As Alastair McNeill, a former consultant surgeon but by then Medical Director at Stirling Royal Infirmary, said in his annual report for 1994:

> Rapid change often results in a degree of stress and, within the organisation, there will be areas where staff are stressed. It may be among secretaries, technicians or catering staff; it may be among doctors and nurses, and we feel it important that, as an organisation, we learn to recognise and respond to that.

Greater public awareness of the health service (whether actually well informed or not) inevitably led also to increasing public expectation. What had been viewed as wonderful when the National

Health Service started in 1948 was, by the 1990s, often seen as not good enough. As one doctor said, 'After World War Two people came out of hospitals grateful to be alive. Now, death is someone else's fault. All death is premature . . . people's attitudes and expectations have changed'. As this change grew, and every improvement introduced cost ever more money, medium-sized hospitals like Stirling began to struggle to meet public expectations.

The new Queen Elizabeth wing was, itself, a good example of these changes already happening. Its opening marked the end of the Clackmannan County Hospital's surgical work and all patients were now sent to Stirling. This meant that the surgeons who had previously split their time between the two hospitals could now be centred only at Stirling. The gradual merging of Forth Valley hospitals was beginning.

Meanwhile, at Stirling's new Queen Elizabeth wing, the Casualty Department (for the expression 'Accident and Emergency' was not yet used) was 'all stainless steel' as one nurse put it. It was modern, and different. Change was happening and it was not easy for some staff used to the 'old' ways to accept immediately.

Happily one change which took longer to happen was the growth of the social problems which eventually came to affect casualty departments all over Britain. 'There didn't seem to be any drink or drugs in those early days at Stirling's Casualty' recalls one nurse. 'Pubs still closed at 10 o'clock then, and people still had respect for our uniform. There were also fewer patients in Casualty than today, so the pressure was less. And if there were any difficulties the ambulance drivers would usually help us – they were tremendous.'

Inside the new wing change was everywhere. One major change was the introduction of a new kind of ward which had small rooms and bays, graded round the ward from low-maintenance patients to high dependency and even intensive care. These ranged from single-bed rooms to others with four or six beds, but they still provoke argument today among people who worked there in 1989. While different levels of attention could be given to different bays, the system prevented nurses, especially at night, from keeping watch over an entire ward (as they could in the older Nightingale wards). Elderly patients sometimes fell out of bed when going to the toilet at night, and then could not always call for help (although this was later improved by using better designed beds with side rails on them). Even the push-button call system did not always work, which left some patients vainly trying to attract a nurse's attention from the recesses of a bay.

Such changes required completely new training for the staff. Gone were the days when nurses could work in any department from surgical, paediatric or ENT to general medical or obstetrics. Nurses now had to specialise in such areas as casualty, orthopaedics, general surgery, intensive care and so on. This may have been progress and certainly offered nurses a better career path, but it made some nurses of that time feel that their all-round skills were no longer valued – they needed to be specialists now. Some of the nurses felt that this broke up the feeling of team-spirit among nurses and divided the staff. As one nurse said, 'Now Sister Rena Horne wore a navy blue suit and was Management, no longer one of us'.

As staff unity loosened, so did participation in staff events – people didn't know the staff in other departments any more, so they did not attend all-staff occasions as they once did. Even the Friends of Stirling Royal Infirmary's long established and popular fund-raising coffee mornings declined as, with no Matron to hold the nurses together as one team, staff participation in Friends events dropped.

Meanwhile, under the new Trust's management, more facilities were added to Stirling Royal Infirmary throughout the 1990s, in a constant battle to catch up with growing expectation and demand. In 1992 the old wartime huts were finally demolished and replaced with a modern Psychiatric ward. In September 1993 a new endoscopy and day surgery unit opened, funded by that Scottish Office grant awarded in May 1992. This also allowed the provision of another anaesthetist and another consultant general surgeon, both of whom began work in 1993, but it also spelled the eventual closure of the Day Hospital at Orchard House in 2002 as, bit by bit, local services were centralised onto one site.

These improvements were then followed by an impressive new Education and Conference Centre opened on 15th October 1993 by Scotland's Health Minister Lord Fraser, and by a £1.6 million upgrade of the outpatients and maternity departments, which was completed in January 1994. By 1994 Stirling was treating an extraordinary 115,000 out-patients per year and was under severe strain, so Stirling's Trust also computerised the out-patient administration system, added 58 more visitor parking spaces and upgraded the kitchens – all during the year 1993-94. These improvements were augmented by more in

1995, including the introduction of an oncology service for cancer patients and increased staffing levels in obstetrics and gynaecology.

Were these additions just 'papering over the cracks' of a hospital now bursting at the seams? Looking back from retirement some staff can see now the pressures which Stirling's hospital management faced. As one said, 'the opening of The Queen Elizabeth wing was just a delay – they really wanted a new hospital'. 'They' meant management and the doctors – they wanted the pooling of equipment, skills and staff in one place (the only way it could be afforded or be efficient), but the public wanted a local hospital for convenience (and yet somehow with all the equipment and medical skills of the best hospitals).

Today there is a realisation that Stirling's population could never have sustained a large centre of excellence on its own, and that feeling was already growing back in the 1990s. 'By the 1980s there was already increasing specialisation – Falkirk and Stirling were doomed,' says one retired surgeon. 'One hospital was inevitable. For real excellence you need a surrounding population of about 500,000. Even now the Falkirk and Stirling area only has about 250,000 so it was always a case of balancing local size with the need for expertise. But two hospitals would never have been satisfactory. They would never have attracted enough high quality staff.'

'Take eye care' says one specialist. 'Opthalmology sees so many different kinds of patients, from new-born babies to the very old. It made much more sense to bring all these skills to just one hospital, so it came to Stirling'.

'Take the example of the Maternity Unit,' says another consultant. 'For truly excellent maternity provision you need to be delivering 3000 babies a year – that attracts the best staff and justifies spending on the best equipment. But Stirling and Falkirk were each handling about half that number of deliveries per year. The only sensible solution was to amalgamate them'. But that would have meant no more 'bairns' born in Falkirk or 'sons and daughters of the rock' born in Stirling – hard to take for many people with local families born and bred for generations in the town.

For the moment, however, two hospitals continued. Ironically, however, as Trusts (even if they were both under one Forth Valley Health Board), each was supposed to bid for services against other Trusts, so there was competition and even some mistrust between the two towns as various Forth Valley services were gradually taken over by one or other of the two infirmaries. Instinctively local people did not want to see their local hospital closed or even downgraded, and from time to time this concern hit the press as local politicians and councillors attacked any idea of moving any facilities away from Stirling. On the other hand, local doctors supported the concept of 'rationalised services' which seemed to offer more efficient delivery of care and treatment and better facilities to the people of central Scotland.

One example of this was the question of child care. As the *Stirling Observer* explained, a 'reduction in junior doctors' hours, a national shortage of consultant paediatricians and the fact that in-patient medical paediatric services are currently split between two sites [Stirling and Falkirk] are said to make it difficult to recruit new staff'. Indeed, two paediatric doctors actually resigned in July 1995, fed up with shuttling between Falkirk and Stirling to do their job.

The question then became, which hospital would be chosen as the one paediatric centre for the area? Understandably people in both towns wanted the service to stay locally to them. 'Paediatric decision demanded', cried the *Stirling Observer* in 1995. 'A call was made this week for a quick decision on the centralisation of paediatric services in Forth Valley'. In June 1995 a decision was made to move the paediatric service temporarily to Stirling, mainly because the hospital already had a neo-natal intensive care unit, but it led to an immediate outcry from Falkirk MPs Dennis Canavan and Michael Connarty. Would there be enough beds for the expected 50% increase in children from Falkirk? Would Falkirk ever be allowed to recruit paediatric doctors in order to win back its paediatric provision?

In 1996 local consultant Jack Beattie was featured in the press arguing that: 'My job as a paediatrician is to provide children with the highest quality of safe care. We cannot do that on two sites, and no health professional who knows the situation argues with that.' And so the difference between the emotions of local people and the hard-headed assessments of the doctors began to grow.

In January 1996 the *Stirling Observer* reported that Scotland's Health Minister (Lord James Douglas-Hamilton) had dismissed claims that the £650,000 being spent on a new 29-bed children's ward at Stirling 'means the move to centralise paediatrics to Stirling [permanently] rather than Falkirk is now inevitable'. That then led to more questions.

Would it not make more sense to centralise *all* in-patient children's and women's services in one place? Should trauma and orthopaedics not also be combined in one place?

As before, this stirred up a hornet's nest of emotional feelings. Although press statements talked of 'working groups' and 'a full debate', and how it was 'important that the public have a strong voice in this discussion', many people didn't believe them and public anxiety grew. 'Clackmannan health views disregarded', said one press headline in 1996, for example.

In late 1995, while the Forth Valley Health Board insisted that changes would not be driven by any pressure to cut costs, local trade union official Jim Devine claimed that 'the prime motivation for the review is to meet a government target for Scottish health boards of reducing acute service beds by a third by the year 2000'. For a time public consultations and 'area forum' meetings were held, but in 2003 all women's and children's services were, indeed, permanently located at Stirling, followed by the transfer of all orthopaedic services in 2004.

As the 1990s ticked by, the decision to move to just one acute hospital drew closer. For a time there was talk of retaining both Falkirk and Stirling hospitals by making one a 'general' hospital and the other a 'specialist' centre (although it was never said which hospital would have which function). But then in 1998 the two hospital trusts were suddenly merged into one combined Forth Valley Acute Hospitals NHS Trust and the picture changed again.

As public anxiety swelled again there were reassurances from the new trust's Chief Executive Jim Currie that both hospitals would be retained. Central to the new trust's strategy, he said, was the development of £10 million 'ambulatory care' or 'walk-in, walk out' centres at both infirmaries. 'We are currently working hard at defining the range of treatment and care that will be provided at both centres, which we estimate could deal with five out of every six patients who currently come through our doors'. There was also talk of 'outreach' services for frail, elderly, mentally and physically disabled and terminally ill people at 'community hospitals' to be set up Sauchie, Bannockburn, Bo'ness and Bonnybridge – but at that stage it was still only talk. The tough decision on which hospitals would, or would not, be retained, still had to be made.

Increasingly, however, the argument for having just one acute hospital began to creep into the picture. One report, commissioned by the Forth Valley Health Board, decided that 'the split site covered by the surgeons was not acceptable and potentially dangerous'. As early as 1995 Ian Mullen, chairman of the Falkirk trust said 'I think clinicians do see centralisation as the ideal position in terms of training and quality of service . . .'. In 1995 Dr Malcolm McWhirter, the Forth Valley NHS Trust's director of public health, also agreed that 'clinicians would probably prefer all major specialities to be at one site, but it would be for the board to decide'. David Hird, general manager of the Forth Valley Health Board said, 'If people feel services can go on as before, it is up to us to explain to groups throughout Forth Valley why we *can't* go on as we are and that they would lose services locally'.

It was a case of professional judgements against local emotions. In late 1995, for example, the *Stirling Observer* revealed 'plans to axe all geriatric beds at Bannockburn hospital'. This may have been the gathering of all geriatric beds into one place where people could be better cared for, but local councillor Tommy Brookes was 'outraged' – and as a popular voice of the people, he certainly spoke for many. In the end this move did not happen, at least not for the time being.

When interviewed in 1999, Ian Mullen, now chairman of the new combined Forth Valley Acute Hospitals NHS Trust, said, 'We are determined to be a listening trust – one that recognises that the health service belongs to the public and not those who manage it'. In other words, although the doctors wanted a centralised hospital for all specialities, there was also a political judgement to be made – how popular would it be with the public? Would the politicians ever be re-elected if they voted these changes through?

Looking back, the 1990s were a time of great worries – would Stirling's hospital become an enlarged centre of excellence at the expense of Falkirk? Or would the political judgement favour Falkirk and see Stirling closed? Would the election of Tony Blair's first Labour government in 1997 make any difference? There were also rumours that the answer might be a completely new hospital – Corbiewood was whispered as a possible site, as was the campus at Stirling University, or perhaps the old Bellsdyke hospital at Larbert.

Staff speaking now of that period use words like 'anxieties' and 'frustrations', mainly because they felt that they never seemed to know anything. One nurse said recently, 'If they had kept us in the picture, maybe given us a date, or at least told us if the hospital was definitely going to close or not, it would have been much better'. And yet, through all these concerns, the normal life of the hospital went on as always. Nurses, doctors, auxiliaries, cleaners, cooks, janitors, ambulance crews, pharmacists, secretaries, administrators and all the others who made the working life of the hospital tick, somehow managed to leave their worries and anger at the door and, day after day, simply got on with the job of caring and healing.

By this time the job of nursing had changed almost out of recognition to that of the 1960s or '70s. In September 1996 the contracts for delivering nursing and midwifery education moved from colleges to universities, and a degree course in nursing at Stirling University now replaced the diplomas previously awarded by the Forth Valley College of Nursing at Falkirk. This seems to have changed the 'type' of applicants for nursing – now they needed good academic passes (at least two Highers) from school, rather than have only a good nature and a vocation for the job.

Before long degree-trained nurses were undertaking many of the tasks previously done by junior doctors, such as taking blood or operating the increasingly sophisticated array of hi-tech equipment now found in hospitals (and for which some could be paid at similar rates to junior doctors). From 1999 experienced nurses could even become Nurse Consultants in another significant career path improvement. On the other hand, things like taking temperatures or pulses, emptying bed-pans, changing dressings and generally making patients more comfortable, which for a century had been the standard image of nurses, were increasingly undertaken now by a new breed of auxiliary nurses. 'Aye, they can work a CAT machine, which is great, but they cannae make a bed,' joked one retired nurse recently of her modern counterparts.

The world of the junior doctor was also changing rapidly. As pressure to reduce waiting lists increased they found themselves working longer and faster to meet targets. Many said that this gave them less time to watch, learn and be trained, even although their working time 'regularly exceeded 100 hours a week' as one doctor recalled. On the other hand, when the European Working Time Directive took effect in 1998 it may have affected workers in many occupations, but in hospitals it was introduced 'incrementally' or in stages, and began with the consultants. Junior doctors' hours were not reduced until 2004 (when they were cut to 58 hours per week). A 48 hour week was not introduced until 2009.

In 2009 the Friends presented this mobile ventilator, which enables patients with breathing difficulties like Mrs Sadie Wilson to move around the hospital and so meet up with her husband Jim and her devoted dog Sam. *Photo courtesy Allan Dewar.*

Even the role of the Society of Friends of Stirling Royal Infirmary changed significantly during the 1990s. Out went the popular trolley service of books which used to make weekly visits to most wards – one victim of the fear of 'bugs' in hospitals, for who knew which suspect hands might have held that book previously? Coffee mornings, raffles, Christmas concerts and other fundraising events also went through a spell of low support, leaving the Friends even more dependent on donations and legacies for funds, and the occasional sponsored walk or bingo tea.

On the other hand, changes in the hospital offered the Friends new opportunities to support its work. For example, as numbers attending Accident and Emergency increased sharply, 'courtesy packs' were provided for people rushed in to hospital unexpectedly, and who had no bag of toiletries with them. These packs contained an emergency toothbrush, shaving equipment and other things which patients might need in their first day or two. The Friends also increasingly began to pay for hospital equipment, ranging from televisions, tilt-up beds and pain relief equipment to a clinical skills training centre and the dummy models used to train junior doctors in new procedures such as keyhole surgery. They also provided a toy train for the children's ward and even a garden for wheel chair patients.

So much for the pressures of change. From time to time during the 1990s there were also moments of note, however, as in May 1996 when a middle-aged ENT patient suddenly seized a fire extinguisher and 'ran amok' (as the newspapers put it) in the intensive care unit, discharging the extinguisher at two nurses before being restrained.

In September 1994, following the snatch of baby Abbie Humphrey from a Nottingham hospital, £25,000 worth of CCTV security cameras were installed at Stirling's maternity unit. This was partly paid for by a donation of £1000 from workers at the Caberboard factory in Cowie – indeed fundraising for the baby unit is something which people have always supported. In 1999, for example, a team of firemen raised over £15,000 for the Ross McKenzie Fund, set up to support Stirling's baby care unit by Stirling County and Scotland rugby star Kevin McKenzie and his wife Fiona, following the death of their son Ross. The team of John Noble, Paul Brown, Allan Huntly and Keith McKenzie, all from Alloa Fire Station, speed-marched the 96-mile West Highland Way, held charity auctions and ran lucky dips at local supermarkets to beat the £15,000 already raised by firemen the year before.

That same year the baby unit's skills were fully tested when baby Amy McAinsh was born weighing just 1 pound 6¾ ounces. Born 16 weeks prematurely to mum Nicola from Dollar, baby Amy spent 42 days on a ventilator and had to be tube fed before being allowed home. 'Twenty-four weeks is really early' said senior midwife Mary Gilchrist. 'We just take it day to day for the first few weeks'. But Amy survived and was even brought back that Christmas to visit the staff who had cared for her during those first precarious weeks.

In January 1996 newspaper headlines cried 'SRI swamped by emergency cases. Forced to cancel minor operations'. This followed a cold winter which, in the second week of January alone, saw 112 emergency cases, mostly elderly people suffering from respiratory infections, flu and strokes, plus another 432 people who turned up at the hospital's Accident and Emergency department – a 30% rise compared to the same week in 1995. With nursing staff working extra shifts, agency nurses called in, and surgeons in general surgery, the orthopaedic and ENT departments all having to reschedule minor operations in order to free up desperately needed beds, it was certainly a critical moment for the hospital.

Stirling's Medical Director Alastair McNeill put the unexpected rise in admissions down to a number of reasons. 'Many of them are older people... The cold weather spell we've had must have played some part in the rise but it's also fair to say that [winter admission numbers] have also been increasing nationwide year-on-year'.

In fact this problem continued to press the infirmary every winter. In November 1997 the *Stirling Observer*'s headline was 'Winter of discontent looms for patients. Soaring emergency admissions and nursing shortage spell trouble'. The newspaper quoted Trust Chief Executive Alan Hunter saying 'We've experienced a 65% increase recently in emergency medical admissions, with a further rise likely this winter . . . We are planning to open the same number of additional winter beds this year as last. Seven are already opened and we are hoping to open another 17.'

Unfortunately this coincided with a national shortage of nurses – it had taken two rounds of interviews just to recruit seven nurses for the extra winter beds but, 'We could do with another five trained nurses by the middle of December', said the hospital's Director of Nursing Services, Andrea Star. 'If we don't have them we will open the number of beds we can with what we have. It is all about adjusting the staff across the hospital and redistributing them slightly.'

In March 1996 the D.O.C.S. or 'Doctors on Call Stirling' out of hours home visit service began . As local GP Ian Cathcart said:

> If a doctor has been on call all night and then has to work the following day, he is obviously not at his best. This new rota system will allow doctors more time, not only for work, but also for a better quality family life. In the last 25 years, the number of home visits has increased five times. Since 1990 they have doubled. People are not getting sicker, there has just been an increase in their expectation of doctors.

The service operated out of The Queen Elizabeth wing at the Infirmary, and the green and yellow marked vehicle used by whichever doctor is on duty is still a common sight around Stirling.

Although the DOCS service began in March 1996, that month will always be remembered, above all else, for the truly awful shootings which happened at Dunblane Primary School. At 9.30 on 13th March unemployed former shopkeeper Thomas Hamilton, armed with four handguns, suddenly burst into the school gym where a primary one class was having a lesson. During three minutes of frenzied madness he shot dead the class teacher Gwen Mayor and fifteen little children, all but one of whom was only five years old. Hamilton also shot and wounded teachers Eileen Harrild and Mary Blake and thirteen other P1 children before finally shooting himself dead.

By 9.40am Stirling Royal Infirmary had been alerted to a major incident and a fleet of ambulances, accident and emergency staff and hospital doctors raced to the scene. According to the *Guardian* newspaper, Jack Beattie, a senior consultant paediatrician who arrived with the medical team, said it was the worst carnage he had witnessed in his 19 years as a doctor. "We saw a large number of dead and injured children when we arrived in the gymnasium," he said. "There were a number of teachers comforting the children who were still alive and ambulance staff who had arrived before us. The children were very quiet. They were in shock both because of the injuries and because of the psychological shock."

As doctors and surgeons tried to deal with the wounded, ambulances ferried the urgently injured to Stirling while a helicopter rushed one boy to the Royal Hospital for Sick Children in Glasgow. It was a scene of horrific carnage for which none of the hospital staff or ambulance crews could have been trained or prepared, and which several of those who attended have said will live with them for ever. By 10.30 the wounded had been brought to the hospital where the battle to save their lives continued but where, in spite of desperate efforts, another child died. 'That day is still scarred on my mind', said one surgeon recently, clearly reluctant to speak more of his memories. It remains the worst day in the history of the Infirmary.

Just two months later, in April 1996, the hospital was also hit by an MRSA (Methicillin Resistant Staphyloccus Aureaus) scare when four patients were diagnosed as carrying the life-threatening bug and were put into quarantine. Although these were relatively early days in the spread of this 'superbug' (297 patients died in Scottish hospitals between 2000 and 2006 either from MRSA or because of complications which it caused), lurid stories of this 'flesh-eating virus' which seemed to be resistant to normal antibiotics had already spread enough to cause widespread public fear.

In fact the bug was relatively common in hospitals across Scotland – Stirling had already experienced 52 cases in the previous year – and it was easily treated. Dr Xavier Emmanuel, consultant micro-biologist at Edinburgh Royal Infirmary, said:

> This bug is very common and in fact many people will have the bacteria on their bodies as part of the normal complement of their skins. However, it can be quite dangerous, but not any more so than any other bug. The people most at risk are patients who have just come through an operation or those with an open wound.

Faced with this, the hospital acted quickly and decisively. Doctors and nurses were given nasal swabs to check if they were infected. The four patients, two from intensive care and two from surgical wards, were then isolated, and admissions for joint replacement surgery were postponed (since infection in deep surgical wounds were considered to be the most likely to be life-threatening). And in due course the scare died down.

Unfortunately this was followed by a salmonella outbreak which occurred in October 1998. A patient already suffering from salmonella was admitted to Ward 16 for the Care of the Elderly, where it spread to two more patients. As soon as this was realised the ward was closed until any risk of cross-infection had passed. Happily none of the remaining 26 elderly patients caught the bacteria and less than a week later the ward was reopened, leaving just the three patients with the infection isolated in single rooms while they received treatment.

While the salmonella bug may have caused some concern in Stirling, it was nothing compared to the talk of the 'Millennium Bug' which began to spread in 1998. At that time it was widely believed that computerised information and storage systems, power and water supplies, telecommunications, flight controls, traffic lights and the like would all fail when their computer clocks hit the year 2000. If that happened, hospitals would, of course, be critically affected.

A House of Commons research paper of July 1998 indicates the seriousness with which the Government saw the threat:

> Many computer systems, programmes and electronically controlled equipment are unable to perform correct calculations involving dates which fall after 31 December 1999. This is a result of the common practice in the 60s and 70s of using two digits to indicate the year, e.g. 98 for 1998, to save valuable computer memory space. Unless reprogrammed, bypassed or

replaced these systems will malfunction at the turn of the century, if not before, with wide ranging consequences. This problem has been dubbed the "millennium bug" or Year 2000 computer problem (Y2K).

In response to this the Scottish Office set a deadline of December 1998, by when all 'critical and life threatening systems' were to have contingency plans in place if the computers failed. Further, it was not enough just to have the hospital's computers adapted – what if other organisations' computers crashed? That meant, for example, having back-up generators organised in case power supplies failed. Stirling's Trust responded so well to this requirement (actually putting 'more than average resources to deal with the problem') that it became a government 'exemplar site' of good practice for the entire NHS in Scotland.

In the event, very few systems across the world failed when the critical moment came. At Stirling they celebrated the new millennium in a hospital where everything continued to run smoothly. Some people said later that the whole 'millennium bug' issue had been mostly one of scaremongering, but at the time the Infirmary was ready – just in case.

Once safely into the 'noughties' the relentless pace of change in hospital life continued. In 2002 acute services were reviewed, junior doctors' hours were reviewed (they were allowed a tea break), and day hospital services were moved from Orchard House to the Infirmary. A year later all women and children's services were centralised at the Infirmary, followed by the transfer of all orthopaedic services.

In 2004 the *Herald* reported yet another change when it announced:

Busy emergency unit to be downgraded; Falkirk A&E cases to be sent to Stirling Royal Infirmary.

An accident and emergency department at one of central Scotland's busiest hospitals is to be downgraded and all major trauma cases and serious surgical and medical emergencies will now be diverted to another hospital. The measure was approved yesterday by NHS Forth Valley, which has decided to consolidate all major emergency treatment at Stirling Royal Infirmary while the A&E department at Falkirk and District Royal Infirmary will now deal only with minor injuries, dental emergencies and planned admissions. However, the deal is being seen as a compromise. Falkirk will retain a rapid assessment and diagnostic service, and 70% of the patients it sees at present [will continue to be treated there . . .]

Some services were also moved to Falkirk, including renal dialysis and more recently opthalmology. But then came the announcement which dwarfed all previous change – the decision that one central acute hospital was, indeed, going to be built. Not at Stirling or Falkirk, but on the 320 acre site of the old Royal Scottish National Hospital at Larbert (which had closed in 2003). Of course it was not a sudden decision because NHS Forth Valley had conducted a widespread consultation involving the public and the staff, and Larbert had been widely predicted to be the location of the new hospital. But it still came as a shock to many.

Predictably there was a furious outcry from more isolated, but very vocal, Community Councils in places such as Killin and Killearn. They were understandably concerned about increased ambulance times to more distant Larbert – indeed Killearn began to explore options of using Glasgow hospitals, which were closer. To Stirling's hospital staff the announcement came as a great shock, especially since it was clear that the Trust had already identified architects, a consortium of construction firms, private financial specialists and many other experts to work on the project. Since the decision was clearly a definite one, there was nothing the staff could do about it, and so they fretted about increased travel times to work at Larbert, or whether they would do the same job, or in the same way, at Larbert. It was a time when 'we were very emotional but, looking back, not very realistic', as one nurse said later.

Doctors were delighted. 'Stirling would have withered on the vine if it had not combined with Falkirk into one completely new hospital' said one consultant. 'At the very least, paediatrics, gynaecology, midwifery, renal dialysis and probably cardiology would all have gone eventually to Edinburgh or Glasgow if the new hospital had not been announced', said another doctor.

In May 2006 NHS Forth Valley issued a media release, part of which said:

> NHS Forth Valley today unveiled its plans for the new £300million hospital for Forth Valley. The hospital is the centre piece of the Healthcare Strategy which will make NHS Forth Valley a pioneer in the delivery of Scotland's new model of healthcare. Work will begin on site early next year and the hospital will be open in 2009. The new hospital will be supported by a range of community facilities and improved primary care services in a model which mirrorsthe new way of providing health services outlined in the Scottish Executive's 'Delivering for Health'.

NHS Forth Valley, Chairman Ian Mullen OBE said: "By 2009 the people of Forth Valley will have a new, state-of-the-art hospital providing modern, high quality services. Our vision for healthcare in Forth Valley is in line with national policy. We believe that where possible patients should be treated closer to home in community hospitals and health centres. When they do have to come into hospital, services should be focussed on their needs and provided in purpose designed facilities."

"The hospital will be built on the 130 hectare site of the Royal Scottish National Hospital at Larbert. This site is exceptional and its central location means that the new hospital will be a key strategic asset for the NHS in Scotland." added Mr Mullen.

The new hospital will have around 800 inpatient and day spaces and will provide the full range of hospital services found in a district general hospital. these will include: accident and emergency, trauma and orthopaedics, general medicine and general surgery, vascular surgery, ENT, urology and ophthalmology, obstetrics and gynaecology, medical and surgical paediatrics, adult mental health, old age psychiatry, medicine for the elderly, renal services including dialysis, cancer and palliative care. Inpatient services will be supported by a wide range of outpatient, day treatment, day surgery, diagnostic and therapy services.

From then on, events moved rapidly. By November 2006 the old RSNH buildings were gone and the site was nearly ready for work to begin. By March 2007 detailed planning permission from Falkirk Council was in place and the Scottish Executive Health Department had approved the hospital's business case. 'There are now no major obstacles to overcome,' said NHS Forth Valley chairman Ian Mullen. ' . . we look forward to construction starting on site later this spring'.

By May 2007 construction work had begun and on 2nd November that year the foundations were officially laid when Ian Mullen put the finishing touches to the theatre block by smoothing the concrete

NHS Forth Valley Chairman Ian Mullen lays the foundations of the new hospital on November 2nd 2007.

with a specially inscribed silver trowel. By now the site was the largest building project in Scotland, employing over 1500 construction workers and more than 100 other staff. The internal floor area of the building was 95,000 square metres. Even the site's temporary perimeter fence was 3.5 km long.

Meanwhile, in spite of the introduction of 'transitional arrangements' in 2005, normal life continued at Stirling Royal Infirmary. In some departments the number of doctors grew – in 1980 there were five radiologists in Forth Valley (two at Stirling, two at Falkirk and one 'floater' who went wherever he was most needed), but by 2005 this number had increased to eight because of growing demand. Similarly, in 1980 there were four orthopaedic surgeons but by 2005 this was up to ten. Euro-legislation also required an increase in the number of junior doctors once their working hours were reduced. Without more doctors, a 24-hour service could not have been sustained.

There were also social changes. As late as the 1980s the hospital staff all knew each other, and so they sported and danced and generally socialised with each other. This declined during the 1990s and into the new century. Nurses saw less of others in different specialities and so they drifted apart. As more women doctors entered hospital medicine and eventually became consultants they chose to go home to their families after work. Gradually the golf and sailing and theatre visits which consultants shared with their colleagues declined until they were but 'ships that pass in the night' as one consultant put it.

Meanwhile, even though its future role was still unclear at that time, Stirling's hospital continued to need improvements, upgrades and new equipment throughout its last years. Some of this was provided by the Society of Friends of Stirling Royal Infirmary. In 1999 they donated mammography equipment, slit lamps for the Ophthalmology department, and refurbished ward 9. In 2000 they provided electrically operated beds, followed by refurbishing relatives' rooms in 2001, high dependency mattresses in 2002, recliner chairs and pain management equipment in 2003, cooling units for the maternity ward, mini-ultra sound equipment and a microscope in 2004, electrically operated orthopaedic beds in 2006, portable ultra-sound equipment for anaesthetists in 2007, furniture for the surgical discharge area, an upgrade of the bereavement area, and televisions for several wards in 2008, a mobile ventilator unit in 2009 . . . and so on, in an amazing continuation of support first begun in 1948.

As the decade moved on, the future of the hospital site at Livilands became an increasingly important local issue. Promises in the 1990s that the infirmary would *not* be closed proved to be true when it was announced that the sites at both Falkirk and Stirling would become 'community hospitals'. These would deal with areas of medicine not covered by the new hospital at Larbert and would be more local in many respects. However the 'royal' name would disappear from both Falkirk and Stirling.

From the spring of 2008, as Britain went through a dreadful economic 'crunch', high hopes and good intentions had to be scaled back. For a time there was talk of levelling the entire Livilands site and building a new, purpose-built centre, but this proved too expensive. Some people spoke of retaining James Millar's original building of 1928 – although it did not actually meet Historic Scotland's criteria to become a 'listed building' and also lay outwith the Randolph Road conservation area, there was a strong sentimental attachment to it. The Queen Elizabeth Wing, on the other hand, was accepted as being worn out, even after only twenty-odd years of service, such had been the heavy demand on its facilities.

Cabinet Secretary for Health and Wellbeing, Nicola Sturgeon visiting the site of the new Forth Valley Royal Hospital on August 13th, 2008.

Opening of a new Dermatology Centre at SRI on May 15th 2006, by Andy Kerr MSP, Minister for Health and Community Care. Pictured left to right are Stirling MSP Sylvia Jackson, Andy Kerr, NHS Forth Valley Consultant in Dermatology, Colin Morton and NHS Forth Valley chairman Ian Mullen OBE.

In April 2011 the future role of Stirling Community Hospital was made much clearer by a press release from the Forth Valley Health Board which included:

> [The new community hospital] will ensure local people from across Stirling continue to have access to a wide range of health services, including a new Minor Injury Unit. This unit will provide treatment for a wide range of common injuries such as sprains, cuts, minor burns and broken bones.

> Stirling Community Hospital will also continue to be a base for hundreds of NHS staff and handle more than 200,000 patient appointments each year, maintaining an important presence at the heart of the community

> It will provide a wide range of outpatient services including a minor injury unit, GP out-of-hours services, X ray and ultrasound, women's health including ante and post natal care, dermatology, physiotherapy, sexual health, a diabetes day centre and audiology.

Although no timescale was given, this included the intention to move some services from Bannockburn Hospital to the new Stirling Community Hospital.

While Stirling's future role gradually became clearer, work at Larbert progressed on the new hospital. In January 2010 the £300 million hospital was granted the royal seal of approval – 135 years after Stirling received its own seal of royal approval from Queen Victoria in November 1874. This meant the new building at Larbert could now be known officially as the Forth Valley Royal Hospital.

Thereafter, more events marked the Larbert hospital's progress. In February 2010 the development of 70 acres of green space and woodland around the hospital building was announced, in an imaginative collaboration with the Forestry Commission Scotland. Forestry Commission ranger Gordon Harper started work to encourage patients, visitors, staff and the local community to make more use of the hospital's woodlands – the first such service at any hospital in Scotland.

In May 2010 a time capsule filled with items relating to health care in Scotland between 1850 and 2010 was buried in the visitor garden of

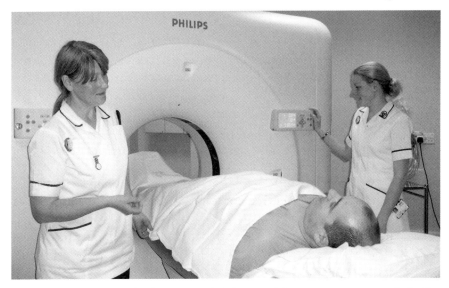

In 2007 Stirling Royal Infirmary took delivery of this super scanner on behalf of NHS Forth Valley Health. At a cost of £500,000 it could take nearly 500 pictures of a human chest in 5 or 6 seconds. It could scan a slice of a body part as finely as 0.6mm – that is the thickness of a leaf or the petal of a flower.

Midwives from some of the world's poorest countries visit the clinical skills
simulation centre at Stirling Royal Infirmary during summer 2008 where they
exchanged views and practice methods with staff and met NHS Forth Valley
executives. Pictured with them are Director of Nursing Angela Wallace
(left) and Clinical Risk Management Co-ordinator Breda Seaman.

the hospital. In the September 2010 a specially commissioned painting
by talented local artist Alex McMillan was unveiled. It shows the
hospital building surrounded by nature in vibrant colours and under
a striking sky. The painting now hangs in the hospital's restaurant.

In June 2010 came the startling announcement that robots would
be used in the hospital. Today they are an everyday part of the
hospital's work – indeed local schools have even adopted and named
some of them. Using laser technology to guide themselves around the
hospital's underground service corridors, these fully automated five
foot tall machines, resembling mini fork lift trucks, trundle between
wards carrying bed linen, waste and medical supplies. The machines
are loaded and unloaded in a basement area and make their deliveries
to wards via a number of separate lifts and corridors with separate
flows for clean and dirty goods. In the unlikely event that a robot fails,
an electric vehicle can be summoned to tug the robot out of trouble.
And should there be problems with one particular lift the robots can
be re-routed through a special sensor system. There is also a fleet of 13

First Minister Alex Salmond at the FVRH topping out ceremony on March 20th, 2009

separate robots to help meet demand during peak periods and provide back-up, if required.

According to a press release the new hospital was also at the cutting edge of new ideas in other respects:

> The supply robots are only part of the brave new world which will operate in Forth Valley Royal Hospital. Other innovations include a fully robotic pharmacy system, capable of labelling medicines as well as stocking supplies and picking up drugs. The system is not only quicker and more efficient but also makes the dispensing process safer still. Robotic equipment will also be used to clean the hospital's 16 hi-tech operating theatres. In addition, the hospital will be equipped with two of the most advanced CT scanners, an MRI scanner and seven digital X-Ray rooms, a first for Forth Valley.

If the ghosts of Stirling's hospital founders are watching, they must be amazed at the changes which have occurred in local health care over the past 135 years!

In August 2010 the hospital's Mental Health Unit was completed and, with the transfer of acute inpatient mental health services from Falkirk and Stirling, the Unit opened for patients in September 2010

James Millar's hospital building of 1928, the original centrepiece of the
Infirmary at Livilands, as it looked in April 2011. *Photo Craig Mair*

(although outpatient care continued to be provided at Falkirk, Alloa
and Stirling). The Unit contains 94 beds in five wards and is expected
to treat around 4000 inpatients a year, including liaison psychiatry.
Users and carers were involved in its design, which includes light and
airy single rooms with en-suite facilities, enclosed courtyards with
plants and benches, accommodation for patients with special
requirements such as mothers with babies, a gym, visitor rooms,
therapy rooms, quiet sitting rooms and its own separate dining, sitting
and activity areas.

And so with patients now being treated there, life at Larbert began
to grow. In October 2010 the WRVS opened a café at the hospital,
with their traditional tea and scones included on the menu. On 16th
November 2010 the hospital's restaurant was officially opened by
celebrity chef Nick Nairn, who cooked up a tasty dish of chicken and
vegetable teriyaki stir-fry for the occasion. The restaurant was designed
to have the hospital staff sharing the same facility with visitors and
day-patients – very different from Stirling. Then in early 2011
Scotland's first hospital-based M&S Simply Food store and café
opened, so catering is certainly well provided for at Larbert!

Bit by bit staff began to transfer to the new hospital. For some the
sheer scale of the new building was a surprise, 'but I'm beginning to
find my way around now' said one nurse. For others there was
undoubtedly some anxiety about moving to such a different

In July 2010 volunteers at the WRVS café in Stirling Royal Infirmary handed over a cheque for an astounding £100,000, raised through serving gallons of tea and coffee, tens of thousands of scones and pancakes, and a range of other goodies. The money went to help fund a range of activities for patients across Forth Valley, including arts and craft work, day trips and theatre outings and Christmas parties.

The last Christmas celebrations to be held in the children's ward at Stirling Royal Infirmary kicked off with a visit by the Falkirk football team and their mascot.

environment from Stirling. 'I'm still getting used to all the space around the hospital building,' said another nurse. 'It's a very different feel for a working area, both inside and out, but although I was very happy at Stirling, this is exciting and new and it's growing on me'.

Soon the hospital was a busy place. 'Well we're certainly working on the waiting lists!' said one nurse in March 2011. 'People come in here for operations and they're often out the same day. Hernias used to need ten days in a bed, six before the stitches came out and then more to recover. Now the patients leave on the same day – walking a bit like John Wayne perhaps, but they're out!'

Doctors also have their views. 'I think it's a great place,' says one consultant surgeon. 'But then, I never worked at Stirling or Falkirk, so I don't have the emotional attachment to Stirling which others have. I can understand their feelings, but we've got great facilities here and it can only be much better than anything at Stirling or Falkirk.'

'I love it here,' says an anaesthetist. 'I worked for 20 years at Stirling but in the long run it would never have succeeded alone. It had to join with Falkirk on a new site. Now it's great.'

'Urologists have been asking for this for twenty years,' says a retired consultant. 'Now they can work in one place without wasting time going back and forth between hospitals. Now they'll have the best equipment, the best arrangements – they must be really pleased.'

'It will take time to settle in,' says a retired senior nurse, 'but it secured specialist services within Forth Valley and that's great. Except neuro-surgery – they only do that at Edinburgh, Glasgow and Aberdeen. It's all to do with economies of scale.' Then with a smile the nurse adds, 'But the discipline has changed. It's all informal now. That's okay if it's not abused, but if I was working at Larbert I don't think I'd ever get used to calling consultants by their first names!'

And so the staff, some excited and some with trepidation, began to adjust to their new environment. Bit by bit Stirling people got used to being sent to Forth Valley Royal Hospital for many of their medical conditions. For others, however, their treatment continued to be centred at Stirling, for some departments were not transferred to Larbert. Change has *not* erased hospital care from the town and that thread of history has certainly not been cut. Following the transfer of acute services, including Accident and Emergency, from Stirling to Larbert between July 11th and 18th 2011, Stirling Royal Infirmary began a new life as Stirling Community Hospital, and so the thread continued.

By early 2011 parts of the former Falkirk and District Royal Infirmary were already being demolished. The Friends of Falkirk Royal Infirmary decided to disband and switch support to the new Friends of Forth Valley Royal Hospital. The Friends of Stirling Royal Infirmary considered doing likewise but decided, instead, to continue their work in Stirling. And so when it opened in July 2011, Stirling Community Hospital's staff and patients were able to count on the continued support of the Friends.

On Wednesday 6th July the Forth Valley Royal Hospital was officially opened by Her Majesty Queen Elizabeth, accompanied by the Duke of Edinburgh. Despite heavy rain, large flag-waving crowds came to glimpse the Queen as she entered the new hospital building

Heather presents her posy to the Queen

and met staff, patients, volunteers and various dignitaries gathered in the main atrium. Her Majesty was presented with a posy by 8-year-old Heather Inglis from Blair Drummond. Heather, once a patient in the special baby care unit at Stirling Royal Infirmary, raised £600 by helping to host a fundraising day at her father's farm to say thank you to the nursing staff. As well as unveiling a plaque to commemorate the occasion, the royal couple toured part of the hospital building. While Prince Philip watched the hospital's innovatory robots at work, the Queen visited the physiotherapy gym and the oncology department where she met some of the patients receiving chemotherapy.

On Monday 11th July the last few babies were born at Stirling's Maternity Unit, just hours before the transfer of the service to Larbert. The last ten 'sons and daughters of the rock' were all presented with a cuddly toy, a commemorative certificate and a cotton top inscribed with the words ' Stirling Royal Infirmary – Special Delivery' to mark the end of an era.

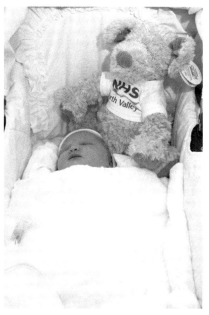

What of the future? Today Stirling is a very different place from the burgh which first saw a hospital open in 1874. The community togetherness which prompted that first group of concerned people – ranging from a coal merchant and a newspaper man to several knights and lords – to provide a hospital for the town, has changed. That first infirmary

Baby Lucy Finnigan, born at 4.21pm on the last day of Stirling's maternity unit before its transfer to the Forth Valley Royal Hospital at Larbert.

building in Spittal Street is still there, but it is being redeveloped as a modern hotel. The nurses, doctors and patients who were its life have long gone. Most shops in Stirling are now chain stores and multinational outlets which no longer share the community spirit to support and donate to the Infirmary as local shops once did. But the town's *people* still do charity walks, and hold ceilidhs and fashion shows, and run marathons, and dress up in silly clothes to support their hospital. The hospital *is* still there in the community.

Today the old Infirmary has a new name, Stirling Community Hospital. It is a good name, for it is a hospital built on land first purchased with money raised by the entire local community in 1928. It is the continuation of a hospital which has been supported by the local community since it first opened in 1874, from subscriptions, Infirmary Weeks and garden fetes to Christmas gifts, concerts, Egg Weeks and dances. From radios donated by the *Stirling Observer's* youngest readers to televisions donated by the Society of Friends.

In return, the hospital has also, for 137 years, seen generations of people who have truly cared *for* Stirling's people – matrons, doctors, anaesthetists, nurses, ambulance drivers, administrators, subscribers, porters, cleaners, cooks, chaplains, volunteers and many more, in an unbroken chain of dedication and service to the community. The name Stirling Royal Infirmary may now be gone, but its spirit lives on at Stirling Community Hospital.

NHS Forth Valley Chairman Ian Mullen outside Stirling Royal Infirmary with a group of nurses wearing uniforms from across the time span of the hospital's history.